D1462408

THE TRUE STORY OF ALUMINUM

ALFRED COWLES

THE TRUE STORY
OF ALUMINUM

Henry Regnery Company
Chicago   *1958*

MANUFACTURED IN THE UNITED STATES OF AMERICA

LIBRARY OF CONGRESS CATALOG CARD NUMBER 58-5756

Contents

Preface

A general impression prevalent among those who have heard about the early history of the aluminum industry is that the modern process for producing the metal was discovered in 1886 by a young man named Charles Martin Hall who thereafter became chief inventor for the Pittsburgh Reduction Company, predecessor to the Aluminum Company of America. Few people know that Eugene Hutchinson Cowles (pronounced Kōlz) and his brother, Alfred, in 1885 established at Cleveland the first electric smelting plant in the world, and that the incandescent electric furnace which they invented, the first to achieve commercial success in the reduction of ore, embodied the same principles as the one universally employed to this day in the aluminum industry.

Recently I was inspired by this apparent contradiction to undertake an investigation in order to determine, if possible, the facts regarding discovery about 70 years ago of the process still used today in the production of aluminum. It developed that significant information on this subject was to be found in the testimony taken and decisions rendered in various important court cases, mainly concerned with patent litigation. Another useful source was the texts of a large number of patents covering processes and paraphernalia designed for use in the production of aluminum which had been issued in the United States and Europe during the latter part of the nineteenth century. Valuable information was also found in the evidence presented at certain hearings in the United States Patent Office where patent applications were in "interference" with each other, or where one was being rejected because of a "reference" to the work of some earlier inventor.

Examination was made of many books and other publications dealing with the history of aluminum, and also of letters and other records in possession of the Cowles family, some of which are of considerable historical interest. I wish to thank the Cowles Chemical Company of Cleveland, Edwin Cowles of Cayuga, New York, and also other members of the family, for making this latter material available. Finally, for guidance in legal matters I am especially indebted to Lynn A. Williams, Chicago patent attorney and formerly a vice president of the University of Chicago. The story, as it was pieced together from these various sources, is quite different from the generally accepted version.

ALFRED COWLES

September 15, 1957

THE TRUE STORY OF ALUMINUM

Chapter I
Historical Background

Aluminum in the latter part of 1957 may have overtaken copper as the second most important metal in the world on the basis both of tonnage and value of metals consumed by industry. The leading position, of course, is still occupied by iron. Of the three, copper is thought to have been known the longest. Neolithic man discovered and began to use it in the late Stone Age, probably about 10,000 years ago.[1] In the beginning certain deposits of pure copper were found and used as a substitute for stone in the fashioning of crude hammers and knives, the metal's malleability making it relatively easy to beat into the desired shape. Some time after 6000 B.C. the discovery was made that it could be melted in fire and cast into the required form. As early as 5000 B.C. copper weapons and other implements were left in Egyptian graves for use of the dead. Bronze, an alloy of copper with tin, was the first metallic compound employed by man, making its appearance about 3700 B.C. It was prized because of being tougher and harder than copper and was used so extensively in prehistoric times that the period is known as the Bronze Age.

Second only to copper in point of antiquity is iron. Evidence of this is hard to get because rust ordinarily destroyed iron or steel implements in a very short time measured in historical periods. An iron blade, probably made about 3000 B.C., was found in one of the Egyptian pyramids. Craftsmanship required for the hardening of steel, which must have taken centuries to develop, was well-known in Greece 3000 years ago and, in fact, is mentioned in the writings attributed to Homer, authorship of which has been set by leading authorities at dates varying from 1100 to 600 B.C.

In striking contrast with the history of these ancient metals is that of aluminum which was first introduced to the public at the Paris Exposition in 1855 [2] and did not come into general use commercially until about 1891. Aluminum is valuable because of its high thermal and electrical conductivity and resistance to corrosion, but light weight is its outstanding virtue. It weighs about two-fifths as much as zinc, one-third as much as steel, three-tenths as much as copper, and one-quarter as much as lead. The advantages of lightness are obvious in household utensils, tall buildings, and all forms of transportation. Weight for weight, aluminum has twice the electrical conductivity of copper, which makes it particularly useful in transmitting electric power at high voltages for long distances. Good resistance to atmospheric corrosion makes it desirable in many uses, including paint pigments, foil wrappings, and architectural features of buildings, and this property, plus lightness and high thermal conductivity, make it ideal for cooking utensils.

In the fall of 1937 the price of aluminum per pound was about eight times that of finished steel and 60 per cent higher than that of copper whereas 20 years later, in the fall of 1957, the price of aluminum per pound had improved relatively to a point where it was only about five times that of finished steel and approximately the same as that of copper. Per cubic foot, by the fall of 1957, aluminum was three times as expensive as finished steel and one-third the price of copper. World production of aluminum has increased at such a rapid rate that in 1957 it is estimated to have been about ten times what it was in 1937.

In this connection it is interesting to note a prophecy made 62 years ago by Professor Joseph W. Richards of Lehigh University who was then a leading authority on the history of aluminum. At that time production of the new light metal was in its infancy, amounting in this country to only 250 tons a year as compared with 90,000 tons of zinc, 181,000 tons of lead, 190,000 of copper, and 10,500,000 of pig iron.[3] Professor Richards said:

At the time of this writing (1895), there are only four metals which are cheaper bulk for bulk than aluminium;[4] viz.: iron, zinc, lead, and copper; and the amount of aluminium produced yearly is increasing much more rapidly than any of these. Aluminium has therefore already won its place among the common metals of everyday life. It will, of course, be many years before it outstrips any of these, but I believe the ultimate goal of aluminium industry will be reached only when it stands next in importance and value of annual production to iron. From this time forth, every year will see substantial advances towards this goal, and the next century may see this end attained.[5]

The correctness of this prophecy is demonstrated in Charts 3 and 4 in Appendix A by the fact that, in spite of aluminum's recent origin, in 1951 it went ahead of lead in world tonnage produced, in 1954 it passed zinc, and in 1957 it may have overtaken copper, thus becoming second only to iron. On the basis of volume rather than tonnage, world production of aluminum already exceeds that of copper, lead, and zinc combined. It is possible that the value of aluminum consumed by industry now about equals that of copper, in which case the prophecy of Professor Richards has already been realized.

Aluminum is the most abundant metal and, in fact, the third most abundant element on the earth's surface, being exceeded in amount only by oxygen and silicon. About eight

3

per cent by weight of the earth's crust is composed of aluminum and its compounds are present to a greater or lesser extent in almost all rocks, vegetation, and animals.[6] In view of this it is surprising that it should be the most modern of common metals. The explanation lies in the highly refractory nature of its ores which cannot be treated by any direct smelting process such as is employed for the other widely-used industrial metals, iron, copper, lead, and zinc. There are two reasons for this difficulty. In the first place, aluminum's affinity for oxygen is much greater than that of the other metals usually present in its ores. If, therefore, aluminum were reduced by a smelting process, these other metals, the oxides of which were present in the ores, would also be reduced and the result would be, not pure aluminum, but an alloy of aluminum with the other metals. The second difficulty lies in the fact that the temperature required to reduce aluminum from alumina (oxide of aluminum) by smelting is so great that, when some less volatile material such as iron or copper is not present to absorb it, the aluminum will disappear as a vapor or else, if sufficient carbon is present, it will be converted into worthless aluminum carbide.[7]

The first attempt to produce aluminum by electricity was made in London by Sir Humphry Davy in 1807.[8] The electric battery had been invented in 1800 by Alessandro Volta of Pavia, Italy, and this for the first time made it possible to produce electric current of effective magnitude, although at great expense from the commercial viewpoint because of the consumption of zinc in the batteries. Davy, employing a "voltaic pile" of 1000 plates, succeeded in isolating potassium and sodium by electrolysis. The *Encyclopaedia Britannica* defines electrolysis as the passage of an electric current through a substance, thereby accomplishing definite chemical changes which are independent of the heating effects of the current. It is not possible to produce aluminum by electrolysis of any aqueous solution of its salts because the critical pressure in the case of water is less than that required for isolation of aluminum and the latter's great affinity for oxygen results in aluminum hydroxide being formed at the cathode instead of the desired metal. For this and other reasons discussed in the preceding paragraph, Davy failed in his attempts to produce the pure metal although in 1809 he did get an alloy of aluminum with iron.

Aluminum was first isolated in 1825 by Hans Christian Oersted, a professor at the University of Copenhagen in Denmark, who produced a very small amount of it by a chemical process which consisted of causing dilute potassium amalgam to react with an excess of anhydrous aluminum chloride, deriving therefrom aluminum amalgam (aluminum combined with mercury) from which the mercury was then distilled away, leaving a small residue of aluminum. He published at the time in a Swedish journal the following description of his experiments:

As is well known, chemistry has succeeded, particularly in recent times, in producing compounds of chlorine and most of the combustible elements. The compound of chlorine and aluminum (the metal of clay) was one of the few of these compounds which were left. In this case nothing could be expected from the ordinary methods of producing chlorine compounds; a new method had to be devised. Dry chlorine was led over a mixture containing pure alumina which was kept at red heat in a porcelain tube. Since the alumina thus had an opportunity to decompose on account of the heat, its combustible constituent combined with the chlorine and formed with it a volatile compound which was easily collected in a condenser, which naturally had to be provided with an exit tube for the unused chlorine and carbon monoxide formed.

The compound of chlorine with the combustible element

5

of the clay (aluminum chloride) is volatile at a temperature which is not much above that of boiling water; it is somewhat yellowish, perhaps however from admixed carbon; it is soft, but still has crystalline form; it absorbs water with avidity and dissolves therein with great ease and with evolution of heat. Rapidly heated with potassium amalgam, it is decomposed, potassium chloride and aluminum amalgam being formed. This amalgam is very quickly decomposed in contact with the atmosphere. By distillation without contact with the atmosphere it forms a lump of metal which in color and luster somewhat resembles tin. Moreover the author has found, both in the amalgam and the aluminum, remarkable properties which do not permit him to regard the experiment as complete; but show promising prospects of important results.[9]

Friedrich Wöhler, born in 1800, attempted unsuccessfully in 1827 to repeat Oersted's experiment. He did, however, by substituting metallic potassium for potassium amalgam as the reducing agent, obtain at that time aluminum in the form of a gray powder containing some impurities. For many years it was thought that Oersted had been mistaken in his 1825 announcement that he had isolated aluminum. About 1920, however, some of his unpublished notes came to light which described in greater detail certain experiments with dilute potassium amalgam and an excess of aluminum chloride. At that time Danish chemists, by repeating his experiments of almost 100 years before, were able to prove that aluminum could be produced in accordance with Oersted's claims.

In 1845 Wöhler, then a professor of chemistry at the University of Göttingen in Germany, for the first time produced enough aluminum, consisting of particles the size of large pinheads, so that its density, color, and a few other physical properties could be determined. Because of the oxide film on these particles he could not make them coalesce. The following is an extract from his description of these experiments:

On account of the violent incandescence with which the reduction of aluminium chloride by potassium is accompanied, this operation requires great precautions, and can be carried out only on a small scale. I took for the operation a platinum tube, in which I placed aluminium chloride, and near it some potassium in a platinum boat. I heated the tube gently at first, then to redness. But the reduction may also be done by putting potassium in a small crucible, which is placed inside a larger one, and the space between the two filled with aluminium chloride. A close cover is put over the whole, and it is heated. Equal volumes of potassium and aluminium salt are the best proportions to employ. After cooling, the tube or crucible is put in a vessel of water. The metal is obtained as a gray metallic powder, but on closer observation one can see even with the naked eye small tin-white globules, some as large as pins' heads.[10]

Electrolytic production of aluminum was first accomplished in 1854 by Henri St. Claire Deville, a professor at the École Normale in Paris, and by Robert Wilhelm von Bunsen, a professor at Heidelberg in Germany. The success of Bunsen with electrolysis of magnesium chloride had inspired Deville to try a similar experiment with fused sodium-aluminum chloride. By this means he obtained aluminum in March, 1854, almost simultaneously with Bunsen who published his results in a German journal just a week before Deville's announcement in a paper which he read to the French Academy of Sciences in Paris. There can be no doubt that the reduction of aluminum by electrolysis was the simultaneous discovery of these two men.

About that time Napoleon III became greatly interested and in 1855 financed experiments by Deville in the hope that production of aluminum might be cheapened to a point where he could employ it to lighten the equipment of his army to such an extent as to increase substantially the scope of its operations. Because the electrolytic process, due to the large consumption of zinc in the batteries, was at that time too expensive for commercial use, Deville abandoned it and in 1855 developed a chemical process in which sodium replaced potassium. By this method Wöhler's pinheads of aluminum could be made to coalesce into lumps the size of marbles from which all of its physical properties could be determined with accuracy. Furthermore, through the efforts of Deville, sodium had become so much cheaper than potassium that by 1859 the price of aluminum was reduced to $17 a pound, about the price of silver, whereas in 1852, at $500 to $750 a pound, it had been considerably more expensive than gold. Even this reduction was, of course, not sufficient to make possible the realization of Napoleon's dream of aluminum armor and helmets for his cuirassiers. An aluminum baby rattle was presented to the infant Prince Imperial which, due to the sonorousness of the metal, was probably very satisfactory. The Emperor gave an aluminum watch charm to the visiting King of Siam, and had forks and spoons of the new light metal for use by his most honored guests at state banquets, but the price was still prohibitively high when judged by modern standards, and it remained at about that level for 26 years until 1885. During that period use of the metal was confined largely to rings, brooches, statuettes, and other ornaments.

Commercial success of the electric furnace employed in the modern process for the production of aluminum depended upon development of cheap electric current of effective magnitude which, in turn, was not possible until the dynamo in the late 1870's "made its momentous appearance." [11] Various other applications of electricity to industry came before the dynamo. The first important commercial use of electricity dated from shortly after invention of the electric battery in 1800 by Volta which led immediately to extensive investigations into the chemical effects of electrolysis and, hence, to electroplating and electrotyping. The latter is a process, used extensively in printing, where some soft material is used to make a negative impression of the object to be copied, this cast being then electrolytically plated with a layer of metal. A practical system of recording telegraphy was perfected about 1838 by Samuel F. B. Morse and in 1876 Alexander Graham Bell invented the telephone.

Development of the electric dynamo began with the work of Michael Faraday in England about 1831 but surprisingly it did not come into extensive commercial use until about 50 years after that.[12] Not until 1866 did Siemens in Berlin and Wheatstone in London, through employment of an electromagnet, overcome certain technical difficulties which had prevented the creation of a sufficiently powerful magnetic field. In the 15 years following 1866 the dynamo was perfected to a point where it could be used commercially, largely through the efforts of Gramme. The fundamental principle of reversibility of function whereby two similar machines are connected in the same circuit, one for generating and the other for reconverting electricity, was introduced by Gramme at the Vienna Exposition in 1873. By 1878 development of the dynamo had progressed to a point where it was beginning to be used commercially for electric arc lighting.

Sir Humphry Davy in England about 1808 had demonstrated an arc light, employing electric current from the so-called voltaic pile, but this was too expensive for commercial use because of the metal consumed in the pile. It was not until about 1876 that development of the dynamo made arc lighting commercially practicable. Charles Francis Brush, who graduated from the University of Michigan in 1869,

9

was the pioneer in this field in the United States. During 1876, when 27 years of age, he demonstrated his first arc light at a public exhibition in Cleveland. In 1878 twenty Brush arc lights, for which the current was supplied by five dynamos, were installed at the John Wanamaker store in Philadelphia. These developments in the United States had been paralleled in Europe where Jablochkoff about simultaneously with Brush in 1876 also demonstrated an arc light. Before the end of 1878 about 300 of these "Jablochkoff candles" had been installed in Paris, the Avenue de l'Opéra being lit by 46 and the Place de l'Opéra by 22.[13] At the end of 1878 they were also introduced in London.[14] In 1879 Brush displayed 12 of his lights in one of Cleveland's parks. This created a sensation as indicated by an account in the *Cleveland Plain Dealer* which said:

Thousands of people gathered . . . and as the arc light shot around and through the park a shout was raised. Presently the Grays Band struck up in the pavilion, and soon afterward a section of artillery on the lake shore began firing a salute in honor of the occasion.

As a result of this demonstration Brush was able that summer to promote the California Electric Light Company which established in San Francisco the first electric central station in the world. In 1880 he founded in Cleveland the Brush Electric Company for the manufacture of electric arc street lighting equipment and the Brush Electric Light and Power Company, of which Eugene Cowles became manager, which operated arc lights in Cleveland. It was in the Brush shops, incidentally, that the Cowles brothers during 1884 constructed and demonstrated their first electric furnace.

By 1883 there were 75,000 arc lights in service in the United States. Pressure to design and produce larger dynamos arose from this source, the six-light dynamo of 1878 being replaced by a 65-light dynamo in 1884. In 1883 a patent infringement suit resulted in a decision that after December 30, 1880, the electric dynamo had been free from patent control, which meant that thereafter anyone could manufacture it.

In the meantime, Thomas Alva Edison had emerged on the scene. He was born in 1847 at Milan, Ohio, and never had the advantage of a formal education. By 1876, however, when 29 years of age, he had accumulated enough capital, through the invention and manufacture of a stock ticker and other telegraphic devices, so that he was able to devote most of his time to research and invention. Edison knew that 90 per cent of the revenues of gas companies came from the lighting of homes and offices, for which electric arc lights were not well adapted. He determined, therefore, to develop incandescent electric lighting which would be more suitable for this much larger field. In the fall of 1877 he began experimenting along these lines and by the fall of 1879 had invented the first successful incandescent electric lamp.

In 1878 Grosvenor P. Lowrey organized the Edison Electric Light Company, the purpose of which was to finance Edison's development of incandescent lighting and to hold title to certain of his patents in this field. Lowrey, who plays a prominent role at two points later in this story, was general counsel for the Western Union Telegraph Company to which Edison had previously sold patents, and the two men had worked together on various infringement cases involving these patents. In April, 1881, the city of New York granted a franchise to a subsidiary of the original Edison Company to lay its wires in the city's streets and on September 4, 1882, Edison placed in operation in New York City the first central generating station for electric house lighting with incandescent lamps which in the beginning had a total capacity of 1200 horsepower and supplied light for houses within a 12-block area.

Following the introduction of dynamos for street and house lighting came the development of water power to operate the dynamos which, where available, was cheaper than employing combustion engines for this purpose. The first use of water power to generate electricity for commercial purposes occurred at Niagara Falls in 1881 where for some time prior to then water wheels had been employed to operate a paper mill and several small factories. Some of the power from the water wheels was for the first time used to generate electricity by the Brush Electric Light and Power Company of Niagara Falls which was established in November, 1881. The *Niagara Falls Gazette* of December 14, 1881, announced that electric light would be furnished on that evening to various local merchants. Sufficient electricity was developed there at that time to operate sixteen 2000 candle-power open arc lamps which were used to furnish street and store service.[15]

Another stimulus to the development of dynamos was electric street railways. Late in 1883 work was begun on an electric railway system at the Brush Electric Company shops in Cleveland. In the spring of 1884 a contract was made with the East Cleveland Street Railway Company to electrify a mile of tracks and equip several cars for use thereon. This enterprise commenced regular operation in July, 1884, and was the first commercial electric street railway in the United States.

NOTES

[1] Information on the antiquity of metals in this and the succeeding paragraph is from the *Encyclopaedia Britannica* (1953 ed.), VI, 401-2, and XII, 649.

[2] Edwards, Frary, and Jeffries, *The Aluminum Industry* (2 vols.; New York: McGraw-Hill Book Co., 1930), I, 5.

[3] U.S. Dept. of Commerce, *Historical Statistics of United States.*

[4] Anglicized spelling.

[5] Joseph W. Richards, *Aluminium* (3rd ed.; Philadelphia: H. C. Baird & Co., 1896), p. 474.

[6] Information in this paragraph is from the *Encyclopaedia Britannica* (1953 ed.), I, 713-14.

[7] Donald H. Wallace, *Market Control in the Aluminum Industry* (Cambridge: Harvard University Press, 1937), p. 509.

[8] Except as indicated, information in this and the nine succeeding paragraphs is mainly from Edwards, Frary, and Jeffries, *op. cit.*, I, 1-12; *Encyclopaedia Britannica* (1953 ed.), I, 714; Wallace, *op. cit.*, pp. 3-4, 8, and 503-5; and Richards, *op. cit.*, pp. 11-13 and 475.

[9] Edwards, Frary, and Jeffries, *op. cit.*, I, 2-3.

[10] Richards, *op. cit.*, pp. 248-49.

[11] Wallace, *op. cit.*, p. 505.

[12] Some information in this and preceding paragraphs came from the *Encyclopaedia Britannica* (1953 ed.), VIII, 188, 198-99.

[13] R. H. Parsons, *Early Days of the Power Station Industry* (Cambridge, England: Cambridge University Press, 1940), p. 3.

[14] Information in this and the six succeeding paragraphs is taken chiefly from Harold C. Passer, *The Electrical Manufacturers, 1875-1890* (Cambridge: Harvard University Press, 1953), pp. 14-21, 78-104, and 225-26. See also John Winthrop Hammond, *Men and Volts, The Story of General Electric* (New York: J. B. Lippincott Co., 1941), pp. 28-30. See also *Encyclopedia Americana* (1955 ed.), X, 118-19.

[15] Edward Dean Adams, *Niagara Power—History of Niagara Falls Power Company, 1886-1918* (2 vols.; New York: Privately printed by Bartlett Orr Press for Niagara Falls Power Company, 1927), I, 80.

Chapter II

Modern Aluminum Process

Developments in knowledge and use of electricity described in the preceding chapter form the background from which emerged in 1884 the electric furnace used commercially to this day for the reduction of metal from ore. In 1884 the price of aluminum was $15 a pound. Seven years later it had been reduced to 50 cents per pound,[1] a price at which extensive commercial use of the metal for the first time became practicable. This sensational reduction of 96.7 per cent in the price of aluminum in just a few years resulted from development of the electric furnace and discovery of the modern process for producing aluminum through dissolving alumina in molten cryolite which has been fused by the same direct electric current that also electrolyzes the alumina.

Up to the middle of the nineteenth century most scientific discoveries were first announced in the transactions of learned societies rather than in the patent offices of the world, but, as an outgrowth of the industrial revolution, there was a notable increase in the number of patents taken out during the period from 1860 to 1890. In spite of this trend it was and still is true, of course, that every invention is an attempt at the practical application of knowledge painstakingly pieced together by pure scientists. This one was no exception and it should be emphasized that it came as the climax of a century's progress in knowledge of electricity and metallurgy achieved by Volta, Davy, Oersted, Ampere, Faraday, Wöhler, Joule, Watt, Deville, Bunsen, Ohm, Gramme, and perhaps 100 other scientists. But the honor of placing the capstone of practical utility on this pyramid of scientific knowledge was won by five young men who in the decade from 1880 to 1890 accomplished the great achievement in electrometallurgy of developing the modern process for the production of aluminum.

Two of the five young inventors were brothers, Eugene Hutchinson Cowles (1855-1892), and Alfred Hutchinson Cowles (1858-1929), sons of a newspaper publisher of Cleveland, who worked as a team. The other three were Charles Schenck Bradley (1853-1929), an engineer employed by Edison in New York; Charles Martin Hall (1863-1914), a clergyman's son who had recently graduated from Oberlin College in Ohio; and Paul Louis Toussaint Héroult (1863-1914), of Thury-Harcourt in the Calvados district of France, who had recently attended a French college and whose father had been employed in the French aluminum industry. At some time between the summer of 1880 and the spring of 1883 the Cowles team, when Eugene was under 28 years old and Alfred under 24, and Bradley when under 30, each independently of the other invented the electric furnace used in the production of aluminum. Hall and Héroult, both in 1886 at the age of 22, are credited with having originated a process whereby alumina was dissolved in molten cryolite and electrolyzed, but for this to be effective it was found necessary to carry on the operation in the Cowles electric furnace, detailed descriptions of which had been published prior to the Hall-Héroult invention. It is a curious coincidence that Hall and Héroult, who made simultaneous identical discoveries, each without knowledge of the other's work, were both born in 1863 and both died in 1914.

Hall stated that his process consisted of dissolving alumina in a fused bath composed of the fluorides of aluminum and a metal more electro-positive than aluminum, and then passing an electric current through the fused mass. In an infringement case involving Hall's patent, Judge William Howard Taft clarified this concept as follows:

More than 50 metals are known to chemists. When one of these is united with nonmetallic substances and the compound reduced to a liquid state by solution or fusion, and subjected to an electric current, which decomposes it, the nonmetallic element of the compound will be drawn by the current to that point in the bath where the current enters it from the positive pole, called the "anode," and the metal will move in the direction of the point where the current leaves the bath for the negative pole, called the "cathode." Metals differ, however, in the ease with which the current can draw them to the cathode; and when one is more sluggish than another in yielding to this influence the one is said to be more electro-positive than the other. Scientists have arranged all known metals accordingly. The only metals more electro-positive than aluminum are magnesium, calcium, strontium, barium, lithium, sodium, potassium, rubidium, and caesium. All other metals yield more readily to the current.[2]

While Sir Humphry Davy in 1807 had proposed the use of electrolysis to separate various metals from the solutions of their salts, this had not resulted in the discovery of how to obtain aluminum in commercial quantities. It was not until about 75 years later that the electric-furnace inventions of Bradley and the Cowles brothers, following development of the dynamo, provided an opportunity for a practical solution. It had been recognized that if aluminum could be extracted from its oxide, alumina, an abundant and easily obtainable source, this would be of great advantage. Yet it was just this form of ore which seemed most stubborn. So when the electric-furnace technique, in combination with the Hall-

Héroult contribution, proved not only practical but also capable of handling the inexpensive and abundant alumina, it produced revolutionary consequences.

The Hall-Héroult idea has been described as the finding of a salt which would (1) dissolve alumina fully, (2) conduct electricity, (3) yield only aluminum and oxygen from electrolysis, and (4) not volatilize or deteriorate on continued use.[3] Cryolite, a double fluoride of aluminum and sodium, was found to have these qualifications. When it has been reduced by heat to a molten state, alumina dissolves in it as though it were sugar in water. The electrolytic action can be so applied to the dissolved alumina as to cause its two components, aluminum and oxygen, to separate, the former flowing to the cathode and the latter to the anode. Because the sodium component of cryolite is more electro-positive than aluminum this process can be carried on at a level where the electrical pressure is sufficient to decompose the alumina without decomposing the cryolite. The aluminum, being heavier than the cryolite, sinks to the bottom of the furnace where it is tapped off. The oxygen combines at the carbon anodes to form carbon monoxide gas, which in turn becomes carbon dioxide upon escaping into the atmosphere.

Natural cryolite is something of a rarity, being found in commercial quantities only at Ivigtut, about 13 miles inland, near the southern tip of Greenland. It is translucent and waxy in appearance and the Eskimos are reported to have referred to it as an ice which would not melt in the summer. The aluminum industry uses a synthetic product which is the chemical equivalent of natural cryolite.

In contrast with the apparatus employed by other inventors, including Hall and Héroult, the novel feature of the Bradley and Cowles brothers furnace was that it generated and applied the heat internally, that is, by passing electric current through the mass of ore. This was an all-important difference. Other experimenters had sought to bring the ore to a molten state by applying fire around the outside of a crucible which thus became necessarily hotter than the ore within, and this led, not only to rapid deterioration of the crucible, but also to its contamination of the bath of ore, thereby stopping the process. The direct internal electric heating overcame this problem.

The discovery of how to produce aluminum cheaply, because of the tremendous increase in its use which followed, ranks among the eight or ten greatest inventions of modern times. In the beginning the modern aluminum process was not envisaged in its entirety by any one of the five young inventors who originated its principal features. It was more than four years after the Cowles brothers and Bradley devised the electric furnace, and more than a year after Hall and Héroult developed the idea of electrolyzing alumina dissolved in molten cryolite, before all the components were first put together and employed experimentally in the modern process for the production of aluminum, and it was almost two years after that before the process was employed commercially.

At the start Bradley was unaware of the essential idea of electrolyzing alumina dissolved in molten cryolite and there also is no evidence that he ever constructed an electric furnace and demonstrated his process commercially, or even experimentally. Héroult did not have the idea of internal electric heat to fuse the bath, and, in fact, until 1889 he abandoned the production of pure aluminum in favor of an alloy process.

The Cowles brothers in 1885 were the first to employ an electric furnace commercially but they used it in the beginning for the production of aluminum alloys. There is evidence, however, that they also were the first to employ experimentally the modern process in its entirety. In one of a series of patent infringement suits between the Cowles and Hall interests, Alfred H. Cowles testified that his company had been experimenting as early as the spring of 1887 with the electrolysis of alumina dissolved in cryolite which had been fused by internal electric heat, but that these experiments had been inconclusive because a native alumina (corundum) had been employed, impurities in which resulted in the production of alloys of aluminum with iron and silicon instead of pure aluminum. He produced as evidence various letters and reports written in June and early July, 1887, by Romaine C. Cole, general manager of Cowles Company, Eugene H. Cowles, and others, establishing the fact that they were ordering and had on hand stocks of alumina and cryolite and that they were then actually experimenting with the process used today in the production of aluminum.[4] At that time the Cowles brothers had not as yet met Hall or heard of his patent application, and it was not until the end of June, 1887, after they had initiated these experiments that they received a copy of Héroult's French patent. That the Cowles brothers were the first to apply the electric furnace experimentally in the production of aluminum by electrolysis in a bath maintained in a fused condition by electric current was stated by United States Commissioner of Patents James T. Newton.[5]

Hall was the first of the group to attempt the production of pure aluminum on a commercial basis, but he did not adopt the Cowles brothers' essential idea of internal electric heating until three years after his 1886 experiment, and he did not abandon his various unsatisfactory mixtures in favor of a bath of pure cryolite until some time in 1890 or later.

The modern process for producing aluminum was not fully described in any of the patents issued respectively to Hall, Héroult, Bradley, and the Cowles brothers, mainly because the Hall and Héroult patents failed to include a practical method for fusing and the Cowles and Bradley patents did not contemplate the electrolysis of alumina dissolved in a suitable bath. The latter feature was the essence of the Hall-Héroult invention but both of these men in their patent applications showed the process carried out in externally-heated crucibles employing for electrolysis less current per pound of aluminum than would have been required to fuse the bath by internal electric heat. They did not in the beginning understand the fundamental relationship between electrical heating and electrolysis which requires that loss of heat from the crucible and ore must be balanced by heat generated by the flow of electric current, and that this balance must be achieved at a voltage within the range of the desired electrolytic action. If, for example, the current were increased simply by increasing the voltage, then the amount required for heating might rise above the upper limit of the voltage suitable for electrolysis.

The Cowles brothers in 1885 demonstrated to the scientific world for the first time in history a practical apparatus whereby internal electric heat was applied in the fusing of ore.[6] If Hall or Héroult had realized that through employment of the Cowles incandescent electric furnace, and through arriving at the correct balance between requirements for electrolysis and those for heating, they could have internally fused the bath by the same electric current which accomplished the electrolysis, they would hardly have shown in their patent applications the impractical externally-heated crucibles that were there described. They would at least have been prudent enough to mention as an alternative the possibility of fusing by internal electric heat because under United States law a patent can be invalidated for not describing a usable process.

Solution of the fusing problem was pointed out to Hall by Alfred H. Cowles in the summer of 1887, but Hall did not adopt this suggestion until 1889, two and a half years after his patent application was filed, and after it had been rewritten for the last time. Hall's patent, issued in April, 1889, did not, therefore, describe the process which his Pittsburgh Reduction Company had found it necessary to adopt by that time.

NOTES

[1] For orders totaling one ton or more of No. 1 Aluminum ingots, at that early date not guaranteed more than 98 per cent pure. Wallace, *op. cit.,* p. 13.

[2] Pittsburgh Reduction Co. *vs.* Cowles Electric Smelting and Aluminum Co., C.C.N.D., Ohio, 1893, 55 Fed. 304.

[3] Wallace, *op. cit.,* p. 517.

[4] Electric Smelting & Aluminum Co. *vs.* Pittsburgh Reduction Co., C.C.W.D., New York, 1901, Complainant's Proofs, pp. 159-64, 196-97, 412, 432-33, 454-55 (decision reported 111 Fed. 742). In the many subsequent footnotes referring to evidence presented in this trial it will be identified for the sake of brevity simply as "E.S. & A. Co. *vs.* P.R. Co., 1901 case."

[5] See p. 61.

[6] Adolphe Minet, *The Production of Aluminum,* translation by Leonard Waldo (New York: J. Wiley & Sons, 1905), p. 116. See also Wallace, *op. cit.,* pp. 508 and 514.

Chapter III

The Cowles Brothers

The family of the two Cowles brothers was well-known in Cleveland. The first of them to arrive in Ohio was their great-grandfather, the Rev. Giles Hooker Cowles (1766-1835), who in 1810 became pastor of a Congregational church at Austinburg about 50 miles from Cleveland in the northeast corner of the state. This church, founded in 1801, was the first to be established in that region, then known as the Western Reserve. Giles Hooker Cowles was born in the homestead at Farmington, Connecticut, where his family had lived for 126 years since 1640. He graduated from Yale College with honors in 1789 and in 1823 received an honorary D.D. degree from Williams College. His daughter, Betsey Mix Cowles (1810-1876), attended Oberlin College, about 30 miles southwest of Cleveland, from which she received a degree in 1840.[1]

Oberlin was the first institution of higher education in the United States to admit women on the college level. One woman, who graduated in the class of 1838 there, was the first of her sex to receive a college degree in this country. Six women received Oberlin College degrees in 1839 and four, including Betsey Cowles, in 1840. She was, therefore, one of the first women in the United States to receive a college degree. She became a teacher, an able associate of William Lloyd Garrison in the anti-slavery crusade, and was elected president at the second National Women's Rights

22

convention held at Salem, Ohio, in 1850.[2] Her brother, Dr. Edwin Weed Cowles (1794-1861), was the grandfather of the two inventors. He also was an early and ardent abolitionist, and was for some time superintendent of the "underground railway" whereby many fugitive slaves gained their freedom. He practiced medicine, mainly at Austinburg until he moved to Cleveland in 1832 where he engaged in his profession for more than 25 years. The Cowles genealogy says:

During his first year in Cleveland a virulent and fatal form of cholera visited the city and surrounding country, creating the utmost terror and depopulating the city with fearful rapidity. Amid the general stampede and wholesale flight which ensued, at the risk of his own life, he stood firmly at his post, administering to the stricken ones, devoting his nights as well as his days to the alleviation of their sufferings. In one instance the whole crew and passengers of a steamboat had suddenly become helpless victims of the plague. Disregarding the entreaties of his family and friends, he bravely boarded the ship and there remained until everything possible had been done to relieve the sick and to fight down the death-dealing scourge.[3]

Edwin Cowles (1825-1890), father of the two inventors, was born in Austinburg and moved with his family at an early age to Cleveland where he spent most of the rest of his life. In 1849 he married Elizabeth Caroline Hutchinson, daughter of Judge Mosely Hutchinson of Cayuga, New York. In 1853 he went into partnership with Joseph Medill (1823-1899) as publishers of the daily *Forest City Democrat* which as early as 1853 was advocating that the Whig Party be replaced by a new one to be known as the Republican Party. In 1854 the newspaper changed its name to the *Cleveland Leader* and the Republican Party's origin in large measure resulted from decisions reached at meetings in the editorial rooms of the *Leader* in the winter of 1854-1855. Medill and certain associates, including Alfred Cowles (1832-

23

1889), a younger brother of Edwin, moved in 1855 to Chicago where they purchased the *Chicago Tribune.* Edwin Cowles at that point became sole owner and publisher of the *Cleveland Leader,* and in 1868 he also acquired the *Cleveland Evening News.* He was postmaster of Cleveland from 1861 to 1866. Immediately after the first battle of Bull Run his newspaper advocated the abolition of slavery. Some of President Lincoln's friends denounced him for this, urging that he be removed as postmaster in an effort to conciliate the South. Lincoln refused to do this, stating that he knew of no law which denied to postmasters freedom to express their opinions.[4]

The success of Edwin Cowles as a journalist was remarkable in view of the fact that from birth he had suffered from an unfortunate impediment of speech caused by a defect in hearing. Until he was 23 years of age the cause of this difficulty was not discovered. It was then found that he never heard the hissing sound of the human voice and consequently had never made that sound. Many of the consonants sounded alike to him. He never heard the notes of the seventh octave of a piano or organ, or the upper notes of a violin. He never heard a bird sing and supposed the music of birds to be a poetical fiction. Under the instruction of a well-known elocutionist of Cleveland, who had diagnosed his case, he achieved permanent benefit.

In 1932, forty-two years after his death, Edwin Cowles was elected to the Ohio Journalism Hall of Fame. In an address on that occasion Elbert H. Baker, publisher of the *Cleveland Plain Dealer,* said of him: "His outstanding views on public questions and the boldness and vigor of his utterances, together with his progressive views on state and local questions, soon made the *Leader* one of the most powerful and helpful newspapers of the Middle West." In the history of the *Cleveland Plain Dealer,* Archer Shaw wrote, "All in all he (Edwin Cowles) was probably the most versatile and successful editor northern Ohio has produced."

Eugene, the older of Edwin's two inventor sons, started his career as a reporter on his father's newspaper. He first became interested in the idea of the electric smelting of ore when in 1876, at the age of 21, he wrote a report on Brush's exhibit in which electricity was used for the first time in the United States to produce light on a commercially practicable basis. At that time Eugene took up the study of electricity in the hope of applying it to propelling railway cars and smelting ore. In that period he bought and studied all new books on electricity and became so engrossed in the subject that he talked and thought of little else. He continued, however, for a few years on his father's newspaper and in 1878 spent some time in Washington, D. C., as its correspondent. A vigorous expression of his somewhat cynical formula for success in journalism is to be found in the following letter which he wrote at that time, advising his father on how best to meet the competition of the *Cleveland Herald:*

Ever since the first of January I have noticed the Herald's name quoted about a dozen times where the Leader is mentioned once. It almost sickens me to see the way things are going on. . . . This quotation business I fear is but the first sign that they will overtake us. There is just one way to stop this. Sail into these big papers throughout the country. Whenever a large paper has a pet theory sneer at it and revile it on every occasion. Pitch into the Cincinnati Enquirer, blackguard old Story of Chicago for the lecherous character of their papers, and laugh at the sophomoric literary pretensions of the New York Post and Tribune. Dispute every hasty assertion that appears anywhere and raise faction and strife on all sides. In general trample on everybody's toes and stir up a row. Let the world know that the Leader is neither dead nor sleeping. To begin with I would mix in the muss between the New York Tribune and Times and any other fight I saw going on. . . . Hoping that you may see the wisdom of this over the present namby pamby course of puffing that the paper is pursuing I will close. . . . Good night. Eugene.[5]

Eugene gave up newspaper work some time in 1880 when he organized and became manager of the Brush Electric Light and Power Company in Cleveland. John W. Hammond in his history of the General Electric Company says that in December, 1880, Brush lamps were installed along Broadway for three-quarters of a mile, the first electrical illumination of the famous street, the operating organization being the Brush Electric Light and Power Company of New York, and that this company also contracted to illuminate Union and Madison squares with a spectacularly successful system of masts 160 feet high.[6] In December, 1881, for the first time in this country, water power was used to generate electricity by the Brush Electric Light and Power Company of Niagara Falls.[7] A few months later Eugene Cowles became seriously ill with pneumonia and in the spring of 1882 suffered a lung hemorrhage. His condition was such that, on recommendation of his doctor, he resigned his position as manager of the Brush Electric Light and Power Company and went to Colorado. This was the first onslaught of tuberculosis and, while his health improved temporarily, he later found it necessary to retire permanently from active work and to spend most of the four years from 1888 until his death in 1892 as a health seeker in the mountains of New Mexico.

At that time the medical profession still held the age-old impression that residence in a high-altitude climate was the best treatment for tuberculosis. It was not until 1884 that Dr. Edward L. Trudeau (1848-1915) established in the Adirondacks the first sanatorium for treatment of the disease and introduced the concept that rest, as well as climate, was important. It took some years for his ideas to gain general acceptance and in the meantime the Rocky Mountain States, particularly Colorado, were strewn with the bones of migrant health seekers, mainly from England and the eastern United States, who had gone there in the vain hope that the climate would overcome their disease while they engaged in such rugged occupations as pioneer ranching or prospecting.

Eugene's younger brother, Alfred, spent the school year 1876-1877 at the Agricultural and Mechanical College of Ohio which later became Ohio State University. While there he attended lectures in chemistry and metallurgy. He then went to Cornell University for the period from 1877 to 1882 with most of 1879 out because of illness. While at Cornell he specialized in the study of chemistry, metallurgy, and physics, particularly electricity. He also found time to be an oarsman, rowing on the freshman eight-oared crew of 1878 which won its race with Harvard, and on the victorious 1880 varsity crew. He was a member of Cornell's varsity four-oared crew in 1881 and captain in 1882. In 1881 his crew, the fastest in the United States, competed in various races in Europe including one at Henley, England, for the famous Steward's Challenge Cup, and also at Putney and on the Danube. Alfred H. Cowles in later life became a fellow of the American Institute of Electrical Engineers and of the American Association for the Advancement of Science, founder member of the Mining and Metallurgical Society of America, member of the American Institute of Mining Engineers, American Chemical Society, United States Naval Institute, and Franklin Institute, and was one of the founders and vice-president of the American Electrochemical Society.

Eugene Cowles, having spent the summer of 1882 in Denver and Colorado Springs, in September of that year went to Santa Fe, New Mexico, to investigate some mining prospects. Two months later he was joined there by his brother Alfred. Among the first ores offered to them for inspection were those of the Pecos River Mine located at Hamilton, San

Miguel County, in an angle formed by the junction of Willow Creek and the Pecos River, near what is now a dude ranch resort named Cowles in the Sangre de Cristo mountains 20 miles east of Santa Fe. This region, incidentally, figures in Willa Cather's *Death Comes for the Archbishop*.[8] Father Lamy, called Latour in the book, in 1851 was one of the first white men to go there. It is traversed by "the lonely road to Mora" which he took on some of his mule-back missionary journeys and it contains the cave, sacred to the Indians, in which he and his guide, Jacinto, took refuge from the blizzard.

About half of the metals in the Pecos River ores were zinc with an admixture of gold, silver, lead, and copper, and they were so complex and refractory in nature that there was no practical way of reducing them by methods in use at that time. There was, however, an abundance of water power in the Pecos River which at the mine had a fall of 75 feet to the mile. It was this opportunity for generating cheap electricity which caused the Cowles brothers to follow up the idea of an electric furnace on which they had done some work about 1880.[9] In the fall of 1882 the idea of an incandescent electric furnace was something entirely new and revolutionary in metallurgy, and even the use of water power to produce the electricity had been introduced for the first time only a year before at Niagara Falls.

During the winter of 1882-1883, in a house rented by Eugene at Santa Fe and in a cabin at the mine, the Cowles brothers prepared detailed plans for the incandescent electric furnace which was to become the basis of their first patent, applied for in December, 1884. They became so convinced of the practicability of their electric furnace idea that they persuaded their father to buy the Pecos River Mine which he did early in May of 1883.[10] They were, however, unable to conduct any experiments of importance at that time because of the unavailability in New Mexico of equipment for the production of electricity.

In those days the atmosphere of New Mexico was definitely less conducive to scientific research than that which surrounded Bradley in the winter of 1882-1883 at the Edison laboratories in New York. John Chisum then reigned as cattle king of New Mexico, and at one time he had as many as 100,000 head of longhorned cattle ranging unfenced in and around the Pecos River Valley.[11] Considerable bloodshed resulted from the fact that this vast herd was preyed on continuously by cattle rustlers based in the surrounding mountains. William Bonney, known as Billy the Kid, the most celebrated desperado in the history of the southwest, had his headquarters in the Pecos River Valley. One account states that before his death at the age of 21 he killed 21 men, having started on his career when 12 years of age by stabbing to death a blacksmith who had insulted his mother.[12] In the summer of 1881, a year before the arrival of the Cowles brothers, he had been caught and condemned to death and had killed two deputy sheriffs in a sensational jail break. Sheriff Pat Garrett was told that he was being hidden by some friends in the Pecos River settlement of Fort Sumner. Garrett about midnight entered the unlighted bedroom of the owner of the adobe house in which Billy the Kid was supposed to be hiding about two minutes before the Kid himself entered the room, gun in hand, attempting to elude two of the sheriff's deputies whom he had encountered outside and who had mistaken him for a harmless sheepherder. Garrett, recognizing him only by the sound of his voice and his silhouette in the moonlight, killed him with one shot over the heart.[13]

In the spring of 1883 the Chiricahua Apaches, perhaps the most terrible fighting men the world has ever known, under the leadership of Geronimo and Nachez, son of the famous Cochise, were terrorizing with their raids Arizona, New Mexico, west Texas, and northern Mexico, a region almost equal in area to western Europe. They had equipped themselves with ample caches of ammunition and the best of long-range rifles and field glasses, and centuries of fighting in the desert had developed the Apaches' endurance to a point where they could travel twice as far without rest and stand hunger and thrist twice as long as the picked athletes of the United States Army selected to pursue them. Furthermore, the Apaches knew how to live off the desert and their great mobility enabled them to obtain fresh mounts whenever needed through surprise raids on remote ranches in the vast territory over which they ranged. When the outbreak of May, 1885, occurred, the "renegades," accompanied by their women and children, never drew rein to eat, drink, or rest until they reached the Black Range of New Mexico, 120 miles east of their San Carlos Reservation in the Gila mountains of Arizona.[14] During the 14 months which followed, this small band of Chiricahua Apaches, which never numbered more than 34 warriors, encumbered by about 100 of their women and children, killed about 400 people in the United States and Mexico. In that time, only two of the Indians were killed. This record was accomplished in spite of the fact that they were being pursued by a much larger force of U.S. cavalry under the able leadership of Generals Crook and Miles, as well as by several thousand Mexican troops.[15]

Conditions encountered by the Cowles brothers in their cabin on the Pecos River were not far removed from the wild frontier and it is quite understandable that they found it necessary to delay the actual construction and demonstration of their electric furnace, and the filing of a patent application, until their return to Cleveland in 1884 gave access to machinery for the production of electricity, and to patent lawyers. Their stay of almost two years in Colorado and New Mexico from 1882 to 1884, on doctor's orders because of Eugene's health, readily accounts for the fact that Bradley preceded them in the filing of his patent application.

NOTES

[1] Robert S. Fletcher, *History of Oberlin College from Its Foundation through the Civil War* (Chicago: R. R. Donnelley & Sons, 1943, 2 vols.), I, 266.

[2] *Ibid.,* I, 266-67, and 296.

[3] *Genealogy of the Cowles Families in America,* 2 vols., compiled by Colonel Calvin Duvall Cowles (New Haven, Conn.: Tuttle, Morehouse & Taylor, 1929), I, 275-76.

[4] Cowles Genealogy, *op. cit.,* I, 553-54.

[5] *Cowles-Hutchinson Letters,* 4 vols., compiled and edited by Sarah Frances Cowles (Mrs. Philip B. Stewart), (Colorado Springs, Colorado, privately printed, 1943).

[6] Hammond, *op. cit.,* p. 41.

[7] See p. 12.

[8] Willa Cather, *Death Comes for the Archbishop* (New York: Alfred A. Knopf, 36th Reprinting, 1951), pp. 64-77, 117-36.

[9] See pp. 54-55.

[10] This mine was not developed to any great extent until the period from 1903 to 1907 when Alfred H. Cowles invested about $100,000 in reorganizing the enterprise and opening up about 360,000 tons of ore containing zinc, copper, gold and silver. In 1918 he sold the property for $600,000. See William J. Hartford, *Biography of Alfred Hutchinson Cowles* (New York: Writers Press Association, 1927), p. 4.

[11] Walter Noble Burns, *The Saga of Billy the Kid* (Garden City, New York: Garden City Publishing Co., 1926), pp. 1-20.

[12] *Ibid.,* pp. 53-83.

[13] *Ibid.,* pp. 278-84.

[14] Martin F. Schmitt and Dee Brown, *Fighting Indians of the West* (New York: Charles Scribner's Sons, 1948), pp. 303-4.

[15] Carl F. Lummis, *The Land of Poco Tiempo* (New York: Charles Scribner's Sons, 1921), pp. 157-214 passim.

Chapter IV

Cowles Electric Furnace

It was after his return to Cleveland in April, 1884, that Eugene Cowles constructed his first electric furnace and early in May at the Brush Electric Light and Power Company successfully employed it for the reduction of zinc ore from the Pecos River Mine. Romaine C. Cole, a Cornell classmate of Alfred H. Cowles, then employed on the *Cleveland Leader,* gave the following account of that first experiment:

We got a plumbago (graphite) crucible, and carbon stick, I should judge about one inch in diameter. We carried these over to the station along with the zinciferous ore which Mr. Cowles had at the time, and we fastened a wire leading to one pole of the dynamo to the bottom of the crucible. The other wire we wrapped around the top of the carbon stick very securely. We then put in a very little ore which was an oxide (of zinc) that had been previously mixed with about equal bulk of broken electric-light carbons. I held the crucible while Mr. Eugene Cowles plunged the carbon stick into the mass of ore and carbon which of course formed the circuit. Almost immediately there was a production of heat in the mass and a reduction of the ore, which was shown by the fact that the reduced metallic oxide was volatilized, reoxidized and precipitated from the atmosphere in the form of flowers of zinc which settled upon our clothing and upon the floor and bench holding the apparatus, making everything white, as if it had been visited by a snowstorm. Then we put in more of the mixture of zinc oxide and carbon,

32

quite filling up the pot, the whole mass of the interior having previously been brought to a high degree of incandescence. We at different intervals added more of this mixture, until we had satisfied ourselves that the ore could be reduced on this principle.[1]

Thereafter, the Cowles brothers worked continuously reducing aluminum, various other metals, and their alloys. As a result of these experiments they took out a number of patents, the first and most important of these having been applied for on December 24, 1884.[2] While they were concerned primarily with developing a furnace in which electrical heating supplanted the conventional combustion heating, they were aware that there was an additional important electrical effect. Their first patent, which was issued in June, 1885, referred specifically to the smelting of aluminum ores and included the statement that the electricity, in addition to heating the ore, also decomposed it through an electrochemical reaction "not unlike the effect produced by an electric current in a solution." This statement was related particularly to experiments with zinc but, of course, showed an appreciation of the fact that their electric furnace could be employed in a dual capacity for electrolysis and heating. During 1885 they applied for seven additional patents dealing with the electrical reduction of ores, and in 1886 to 1888 for three more.

On March 18, 1885, they and their father organized the Cowles Electric Smelting and Aluminum Company which at that time placed in operation the first electric smelting plant in the world. In the beginning this was located at the Brush works in Cleveland and consisted of four furnaces, each driven by an electric dynamo developing 40 horsepower, producing a total of 50 pounds of 10 per cent aluminum bronze daily, which sold for 60 cents a pound.

At an early stage in the development of their electric fur-

33

nace the Cowles brothers invited Charles F. Brush to in-
spect it. He replied that he would come and look at their
furnace but that he considered the use of electricity in that
way to be nothing more than an expensive method of burning coal.[3] Brush was one of this country's leading pioneers
in developing new commercial uses for electricity. His
skepticism regarding the Cowles electric furnace constitutes,
therefore, impressive testimony as to the revolutionary nature of the idea.

During the period from 1885 to 1890 commercial production of aluminum by the Cowles Company was confined to
alloys. From the beginning, however, they conducted many
experiments in the hope of developing a cheap commercial
process for producing the pure metal, and they were convinced that their invention of the electric furnace had removed the principal obstacle to achieving this objective. A
booklet on aluminum, published by the Cowles Company
in the fall of 1885, stated that they expected to put the pure
metal on the market within a year and Eugene Cowles, in
a paper presented at a meeting of the Franklin Institute in
January, 1886, stated that the problem of producing pure
and cheap aluminum was practically solved. He predicted
that before long the Cowles Company would be marketing
it at a cost not exceeding 50 or 60 cents per pound. This
announcement was obviously a little premature, for the
Cowles Company actually did not commence the commercial production of pure aluminum until the end of 1890
and it did not achieve the goal of 50 cents per pound until
August, 1891.

In 1885 the Cowles Electric Smelting and Aluminum
Company acquired a site at Lockport, New York, 15 miles
east of Niagara Falls, where cheap water power was avail-
ble from a tailrace of the Niagara overflow.[4] They ordered
ten Brush 125-horsepower dynamos and in 1886 completed

the Lockport plant. In September of that year the Cowles Company installed there a dynamo, at that time the largest in the world, which had been built for them by the Brush Electric Company. This machine, christened the "Colossus," weighed almost 10 tons and developed nearly 400 horsepower.[5] At that point eight furnaces were in operation and the capacity of the plant was 1.5 tons of 10 per cent aluminum bronze per day, the cost being 40 cents per pound, or $2.50 per pound for the contained aluminum. In that year, 1886, the price of pure aluminum in the United States was $9 per pound. This achievement, of course, was not the equivalent of cutting the cost of pure aluminum to $2.50 per pound. It did mean, however, that the Cowles process reduced the price of 10 per cent aluminum bronze to about one-third of what it would have been if made by purchasing pure aluminum and copper in the open market and alloying the two metals, which was the only other known way of producing aluminum bronze. During 1891, however, as a result of further improvements in the process, the price of pure aluminum was reduced to 50 cents per pound, a level at which it became economical again to produce aluminum bronze from pure aluminum and copper. The cost of the alloy then dropped from the 40 cents per pound level of 1886 to 20 cents per pound.

Incidentally, hydroelectric power development was in its infancy when in 1886 the utilization of water power as the most economical way to generate electric current used in the furnaces was instituted at the Cowles Lockport plant. Seven years after that Hall's Pittsburgh Reduction Company followed their example when in 1893 it first contracted for hydroelectric power from the Niagara Falls Power Company.[6]

In the fall of 1885 discovery of the new electric smelting process was universally attributed to the Cowles brothers:

(1) in a paper by Professor Charles F. Mabery of Cleveland, read at a meeting of the American Association for the Advancement of Science at Ann Arbor, Michigan, on August 28, 1885; (2) in a paper presented by Dr. T. Sterry Hunt of Montreal before a meeting of the American Institute of Mining Engineers at Halifax, Nova Scotia, on September 16, 1885; (3) in an article which appeared in the *Scientific American* on September 18, 1885; (4) in an article in the *Engineering and Mining Journal* of New York on September 19, 1885; and (5) in the *Journal of the Franklin Institute* of Philadelphia in February, 1886. Adolphe Minet of France was a leading European authority on aluminum at the end of the last century. In a 1905 English translation of his book entitled *The Production of Aluminum,* he said:

Only after a considerable number of years, during which the application of electricity to metallurgy seemed to have passed entirely into oblivion, did the Cowles brothers (1884) come forward with a process which yielded, if not pure aluminum, at least alloys containing aluminum up to 20 per cent. The characteristic feature of this Cowles invention is the utilization of a type of apparatus which is styled the electric furnace, and which is rightly considered to be the first great advance in electrometallurgy.[7]

In qualification of the preceding quotation it should be noted that prior to 1886 the Cowles brothers had originated and experimented with several different ways of utilizing their electric furnace in the production of pure aluminum.[8] None of these, however, were sufficiently economical to survive in competition with the idea developed in 1886 by Hall and Héroult.

Hammond, the General Electric historian, reported that out of Cleveland had come in the latter part of the decade (1877-1886) news of the first experiments with an electric industrial furnace, the promoters of this endeavor being

Alfred and Eugene Cowles.[9] Hammond stated that their experiments, begun on October 2, 1884, resulted in the production on October 9 of the first alloy of aluminum obtained in the United States by this method, and that it was also recorded that on October 11 synthetic rubies and sapphires were produced in the Cowles brothers' furnace. He described a new "monster" dynamo, built for the Cowles brothers in 1886, as being of the characteristic Brush open-coil type, with a capacity of 3200 amperes at 80 volts, or 256 kilowatts, which was larger than Edison's "Jumbo." [10]

In recognition of their discovery the Franklin Institute in 1886 awarded to the Cowles brothers the John Scott Legacy premium and medal, presented by the city of Philadelphia to encourage science and the arts, and the Elliott Cresson gold medal, the highest honor given by the Franklin Institute.[11] On only one other occasion had both medals been awarded for the same invention. In recommending the award to the Cowles brothers a committee of the Franklin Institute said:

The essential and valuable novelty of the process is the ingenious application of the intense heat obtained by the passage of a powerful current of electricity through a conductor of great resistance, to the reduction, in the presence of carbon, of the most refractory ores, some of which have hitherto resisted all similar attempts at reduction. . . . This process is applicable to the reduction of all kinds of ores, but particularly to those unreducible by other means . . . ; already aluminum alloys of iron, silver, tin, cobalt, and nickel have been prepared; silicon, boron, potassium, sodium, magnesium, calcium, chromium and titanium as well as aluminum have been obtained in a free state.[12]

In the light of subsequent work by Henri Moissan of Paris and others, this statement should be qualified to the extent that, theoretically, the Cowles brothers could not have produced pure aluminum from a mixture of only alumina and carbon in their electric furnace. Something of a puzzle, therefore, is presented by a statement made in 1888 by Charles F. Mabery, a chemist who from 1875 to 1883 had been on the faculty at Harvard University and thereafter a professor at the Case School of Applied Science in Cleveland. Professor Mabery testified at a U.S. Patent Office hearing on December 4, 1888, that he was aware that, according to the best scientific opinion, the reduction of pure aluminum by heating alumina and carbon was an impossibility, but that nevertheless he could state from his own knowledge that products, obtained by experiments in which a mixture of aluminum oxide and carbon was subjected to treatment within the Cowles electric furnace, contained metallic aluminum in considerable quantities.[13] This was confirmed by Dr. T. Sterry Hunt at the Halifax meeting of the American Institute of Mining Engineers in 1885.[14] He stated there that when the mixture in the Cowles electric furnace consisted of only alumina and carbon the reduced metal volatilized, part escaping into the air, part condensing in the upper layer of charcoal into crystalline masses of nearly pure aluminum and yellow crystals supposed to be a compound of aluminum with carbon. Dr. Hunt said, however, that it had been possible in this way to collect as ingots only a small amount of aluminum. Whether Mabery and Hunt observed aluminum reduced as a result of the presence of impurities in the products introduced into the furnace, or what other explanation accounted for this phenomenon, cannot now be determined.

In any case, there is no reason to doubt the statement made by Eugene Cowles, in his paper presented on January 20, 1886, before the Franklin Institute at Philadelphia, in which he said that he and his brother had produced aluminum in at least three different ways in their electric furnace. There were a number of means whereby they might have extracted the pure metal, either by methods which they originated, or by some variant of the previously-developed processes which had been described in the literature. After all, Wöhler in 1827 had produced aluminum in the form of a gray powder from potassium and aluminum chloride, and in 1845 had refined this process to a point where he was able to make the metal coalesce into small globules. Oersted had announced in 1825 that he had succeeded in isolating aluminum although he was thought to have been mistaken until his claims were verified in 1920 by Danish chemists. Bunsen and Deville in 1854 had employed batteries to produce aluminum by electrolysis of molten anhydrous sodium aluminum chloride. In 1855 H. Rose in Germany, and Allan Dick under the direction of Dr. Percy in England, had produced the metal from potassium-chloride, sodium, and cryolite. Deville in 1859 in his plant at Nanterre had employed aluminum-sodium chloride, reduced by sodium, with cryolite or fluorspar as a flux, thereby reducing aluminum and also facilitating union of its globules.[15]

In all, at least five processes for the production of aluminum had been developed which employed various chemical, smelting, and electrolytic techniques. The Cowles brothers, who were thoroughly conversant with the technical literature dealing with this subject, had probably heard about all of these. They had even originated and patented certain processes of their own which, however, were never employed commercially.[16] In one of these they produced an alloy by subjecting to heat in their electric furnace a mixture of carbon, aluminum ore, and some easily amalgamated metal such as tin, silver, or copper, preferably tin. The tin or other metal was then taken up by amalgamation with mercury, leaving pure aluminum in the form of a powder which could be melted into an ingot.

An alternative process covered by this same patent was to produce in the electric furnace an alloy of aluminum with some readily soluble metal such as manganese, zinc, or copper, preferably manganese. The alloy was then broken into small pieces and placed in a suitable vessel through which a lixiviating liquid, such as nitric acid and water, was caused to flow and leach out the manganese or other metal from the alloy. The aluminum, not being touched by the lixiviating process, remained as a powder which was then melted into an ingot.

One other process has been attributed to the Cowles brothers which, however, they never patented. Robert J. Anderson in a book on metallurgy, after discussing the production of aluminum alloys, went on to say that substantially pure aluminum had been obtained also by a Cowles process in which an intermediate alloy of aluminum and tin was made first by smelting in the electric furnace a suitable mixture of alumina, carbon and tin, the aluminum-tin alloy so made being then remelted in a furnace with lead, the lead alloying with the tin, and sinking to the bottom of the furnace, leaving the aluminum on top.[17] That pure aluminum had been produced experimentally in this way was also confirmed by Dr. T. Sterry Hunt in a paper presented at a meeting of the National Academy of Science in Washington on April 30, 1886.[18]

The paper presented at Philadelphia by Eugene Cowles, which was published in the February, 1886, number of the *Journal of the Franklin Institute,* gave a detailed description of the apparatus which the Cowles Electric Smelting and Aluminum Company had been operating for about nine months at the Brush Electric Company works in Cleveland. This was the first electric furnace in the world to be employed commercially for the smelting of ore.[19]

During the year and a half preceding January, 1886, the

Cowles brothers had worked continuously with their electric furnace, conducting many experiments with various ores and types of apparatus. At the same time they had thoroughly searched the patent and other technical literature of the world, having secured copies of all important patents which had any bearing on the production of aluminum and its alloys. In July, 1886, the Cowles brothers received a copy of an 1884 British patent describing a process originated by Joseph Boguski of Warsaw, Poland, for the electrolytic production of aluminum bronze.[20] They sent an agent to Warsaw, then a part of Russia, who on January 11, 1887, purchased for them for 400 pounds (about $2000) all of Boguski's inventions including his British patent, the complete specification for which had been filed in London on November 8, 1884. Boguski's patent never received recognition as representing an important step in development of the modern process for producing aluminum but Alfred H. Cowles testified in a patent infringement suit that Boguski's agent, Zdziarski, at the London Industrial Exhibition in 1884 produced aluminum bronze by electrolysis of a mixture containing alumina and cryolite.[21] As a result of correspondence with Boguski, Cowles had acquired a very high regard for his accomplishments, having learned among other things that he had translated Deschanel's work on physics from the French into the Polish language. It was apparent to Cowles that the English translation of Boguski's patent had been made by someone whose knowledge of the chemistry involved was far inferior to that of Boguski himself, that the meaning of the patent had been obscured by this faulty translation from the Polish, his native tongue, and that in reality it was the first patent in the world to suggest adding simple alumina to a fused bath.[22] Cowles introduced as evidence the testimony of Joseph Lyons, a patent examiner in the United States Patent Office, that the Boguski patent disclosed the electrolysis of alumina dissolved in cryolite.[23] Lyons stated that the only difference between Boguski's process and Hall's was that Boguski's cathode consisted of a mass of molten copper, resulting in the production of aluminum bronze, whereas Hall's cathode was a carbon plate, resulting in the production of pure aluminum. Neither Hall nor Boguski proposed fusing the cryolite bath by internal electric heat. Probably because Boguski was interested in the production of aluminum bronze rather than pure aluminum, or due to the faulty translation of his patent, evidence as to the significance of his contribution seems to have been generally regarded as inconclusive.

The principles underlying the electrolytic refining of metals were first set forth by an Englishman, Charles Watt, in 1851.[24] James Elkington of a Birmingham firm of electroplaters was the first to utilize Watt's proposals for the refining of copper on an industrial basis when in 1869 he established a refinery at Pembrey in South Wales.[25] While Elkington at that time reduced copper by electrolyzing a clear solution of copper sulphate, the commercial production of aluminum by electrolysis could not then have been initiated because it was not until after 1880 that the dynamo was developed to a point where the fusing of ore by internal heat in an electric furnace became practicable as an industrial operation.

Professor Donald H. Wallace, who until his death in 1953 was director of the graduate program at Princeton University, in his book entitled *Market Control in the Aluminum Industry* made the following comments on the early work of the Cowles brothers in designing an electric furnace which employed power generators for the reduction of aluminum:

The first successful industrial work was accomplished by the brothers Alfred and Eugene Cowles of Cleveland. . . . For this initial task (the designing of a successful electric furnace) and the long series of inventions, experiments, and practical achievements in electrometallurgy which followed, the brothers possessed a rare combination of qualities. Alfred brought an alert mind and a training in science which were evidenced by a distinguished career of several years study at Cornell University. Eugene, also resourceful and ingenious, had acquired much practical experience in metallurgy and electrical engineering, in addition to executive experience as manager of an electric-lighting plant. . . . The part played by these innovators in the electrochemical revolution may be summed up as follows. They built and operated several electric furnaces which were not only successful in industrial application but also provided an arresting demonstration of the possibility of utilizing the electric furnace in a wide range of industrial activities. In their electric furnace they decomposed for the first time many metallic oxides which had previously resisted the most determined efforts of the fuel furnace. They were responsible for the first commercial production of aluminum in the form of alloys on a fairly large scale at a cheap cost. Their work possessed great significance for the development of the dynamo. . . . The success of the Cowles furnaces was followed by a broadcast of their results in the leading scientific journals of Europe and America. Literature concerning aluminum was widely disseminated by the Cowles Company. In attracting world-wide attention to the potentialities of electric smelting by furnishing other workers with both knowledge and stimulus, the Cowles brothers played a leading part in the industrial development of electrochemistry.[26]

Referring to their intensive research during those early years, Alfred H. Cowles testified at a United States Patent Office hearing that he had kept notes on their results and many samples of the products obtained, but that nearly all of these were lost in a fire on the night of June 13, 1888, which destroyed the office of the Cowles works at Lockport, all that remained being four test tubes containing zinc products which he happened to have in his own room at the time of the fire.[27] The unfortunate loss of these records undoubtedly had the effect of obscuring to some extent the importance of the Cowles brothers' contribution to the development of electrochemistry.

After the principles of the Cowles electric furnace became generally known in 1885 there evolved from it many important discoveries, and electric smelting came into use in a number of different industries. Among the items which the Cowles brothers were the first to produce experimentally in a small way in their electric furnace was calcium carbide. This product, from which came acetylene gas for lighting and welding, was first produced commercially by the Electro Gas Company which gave the Cowles Company 12.5 per cent of its capital stock in return for a license during the lifetime of the Cowles patents. The Electro Gas Company in 1898 became the Union Carbide Company which in 1917 represented about half the stock in a merger resulting in creation of the Union Carbide and Carbon Corporation (now Union Carbide Corporation) which is today one of America's greatest industrial firms.

As a result of work done with the electric furnace at the plant of a Cowles subsidiary in England an electrothermic process for the production of phosphorus on a commercial basis was developed.[28] This process, in which bone ash was mixed with silicic acid and carbon and heated to a temperature of about 1400 degrees centigrade in an electric furnace, was first employed commercially by the firm of Albright and Wilson in their factory at Oldbury, England.[29] In 1897 this company built a factory at Niagara Falls under the name of the Oldbury Electro-Chemical Company which produced phosphorus there as licensee under the Cowles patents.[30]

Another notable development based on the Cowles brothers' electric furnace was the carborundum industry in which the principal figure was Edward G. Acheson, at one time an employee of Thomas A. Edison, who was credited with having discovered carborundum, a proprietary name for silicon carbide, an abrasive second only to diamonds in hardness. On September 21, 1891, Acheson established the Carborundum Company for the purpose of manufacturing this product but, according to his autobiography, he incurred debts which enabled two Pittsburgh bankers, whom he designated only as "A and B" (undoubtedly Andrew W. and Richard B. Mellon), to take over his company about 1898, and later to oust him as its president.[31] Acheson in 1899 organized the Acheson Graphite Company in which the Mellons acquired a 25 per cent interest. This company employed the Cowles electric furnace to produce graphite according to a process developed by Acheson. He continued as head of this enterprise until in 1928 it became a part of the Union Carbide and Carbon Corporation.

The Cowles Company about 1896 brought suit against the Carborundum Company, charging infringement of the Cowles patent on an electric furnace used to produce carborundum.[32] Alfred H. Cowles and Romaine C. Cole, former general manager of the Cowles Company, identified certain samples of carbide of silicon (carborundum) as having been produced by the Cowles brothers in their electric furnace in the fall of 1884, and as having been exhibited by Cowles at a lecture which he gave in February, 1886, at the Massachusetts Institute of Technology under sponsorship of the Boston Society of Arts.[33] They testified that after the lecture these samples had been donated to a museum connected with the Massachusetts Institute of Technology where they had been ever since the 1886 lecture. Professor Charles F. Mabery of the Case School of Applied Science in Cleveland also testified that in 1886 he sent a sample of this carbide

45

of silicon, produced by the Cowles brothers in their electric furnace, to Harvard College where it was placed in the Harvard chemical collection.[34] The testimony indicated that the Cowles brothers had not at that time undertaken to manufacture carbide of silicon on a commercial scale, that they had not then known it by the name of carborundum, for it had not yet been so christened, but that they were aware of its highly abrasive qualities. It was not until February, 1891, five years after the Cowles brothers had placed specimens in various scientific museums around the country, that Acheson, according to his autobiography, "discovered" the product and named it carborundum.[35] The court ultimately concluded that the fact that the Cowles brothers exhibited from time to time in various places specimens of what later became known as carborundum strongly indicated an intention on their part not to exclude it from the list of products which might be produced by their electric-furnace process.

This litigation extended over a period of more than 16 years. At the first trial the lower court found in 1897 that the Carborundum Company had not infringed the Cowles patent.[36] On appeal, the higher court in May, 1900, reversed this decision [37] and sent the case back to the lower court which in November, 1900, referred it to a master for determination of the amount of damages to be assessed against the Carborundum Company.[38] About 12 years from 1900 to 1912 were consumed, partly by the master in collecting testimony and issuing his findings, and partly by the court to which he reported for action on these findings. The defendant Carborundum Company then appealed the case and it was not until March, 1913, that the higher court took final action in determining the amount of damages to be assessed against the defendant for infringement of the Cowles patent.[39] The Carborundum Company was required by the

United States Circuit Court of Appeals to pay the Cowles Company all net profits made by the defendant from the day it was founded on September 21, 1891, until expiration of the Cowles patent on June 9, 1902, together with interest thereon and court costs, a total of more than $300,000.[40]

By 1898 Pittsburgh bankers "A and B" had acquired more than 50 per cent of the Carborundum Company stock, and in the process had reduced Acheson's holdings to 22 per cent.[41] He, therefore, lost only about $66,000 as a result of the Cowles court victory, whereas his loss might have been much larger if "A and B" had not absorbed more than $150,000 of the $300,000 loss as a result of getting control of his company.

The position of the Cowles brothers in development of the electric furnace is indicated by a statement of Professor Wallace that Alfred Cowles and his associates had by 1902 come to hold the most prominent position in electric smelting in the United States. In commenting on the Cowles Company's 1913 victory over the Carborundum Company Professor Wallace said that the decision legally established the Cowles brothers as pioneers in electric smelting.[42]

The electric furnace was the most fundamental factor in the development of abrasives which, in turn, were important in many other fields. This is well illustrated in the case of the automobile industry, today the greatest manufacturing branch of our economy in the field of durable consumer goods. The late Frank Jerome Tone, formerly president of the Carborundum Company, once said:

The mechanical perfection of the automobile and the interchangeability of its parts have been made possible by the modern grinding wheel. Practically every part of the automobile must be ground with artificial abrasives at some stage of its manufacture. Take away from the automobile industry abrasives and other products which the chemist has made available to it by the electric furnace, such as aluminum, alloy steel, and high-speed steel, and the labor cost of building a car would become prohibitive. The industry would cease to exist on its present lines.[43]

There were various other industries in which the products were greatly cheapened through use of the electric furnace, but the most spectacular achievement of all was the discovery of how to produce cheap aluminum. Before the modern process was made possible through development of the Cowles electric furnace, aluminum was to the public only a curiosity. Today its output in North America is worth over a billion dollars a year and less than 70 years after the industry was founded it may have overtaken copper, in which case the only metal exceeding aluminum in importance would be iron.

NOTES

[1] U.S. Patent Office interference hearing, Fauré *vs.* Cowles & Cowles *vs.* Bradley & Crocker, January 14, 1889, p. 358.

[2] U.S. Patent No. 319,795, issued June 9, 1885.

[3] E.S. & A. Co. *vs.* P.R. Co., 1901 case, Complainant's Proofs, p. 333.

[4] Wallace, *op. cit.,* p. 509.

[5] Richards, *op. cit.,* p. 339.

[6] Carr, *op. cit.,* p. 88.

[7] Minet, *op. cit.,* pp. 22-23.

[8] See pp. 38-40.

[9] Hammond, *op. cit.,* pp. 103-4.

[10] Edison's Jumbo dynamo was first installed in New York on September 4, 1882. Parsons, *op. cit.,* p. 12.

[11] Wallace, *op. cit.,* p. 510.

[12] Proceedings at April 7, 1886, meeting of the Committee on Science and the Arts reported in *Journal of the Franklin Institute,* July, 1886, pp. 51-56.

[13] U.S. Patent Office hearing, Fauré *vs.* Cowles & Cowles *vs.* Bradley & Crocker, December 4, 1888, p. 142.

[14] Richards, *op. cit.,* pp. 331-32.

[15] Information in this paragraph came chiefly from Richards, *op. cit.,* pp. 246-48 and 320-24. See also Edwards, Frary and Jeffries, *op. cit.,* I, 1-12.

[16] U.S. Patent No. 324,659, issued August 18, 1885, applied for April 23, 1885, by Eugene H. Cowles, Alfred H. Cowles, and Charles F. Mabery. See Appendix B.

[17] Robert J. Anderson, *Metallurgy of Aluminium and Aluminium Alloys* (New York: H. C. Baird & Co., 1925), p. 92.

[18] Richards, *op. cit.*, p. 332.

[19] The paper describing this furnace is reprinted in Appendix C.

[20] British Patent No. 3090 issued in 1884 to Anthony Zdziarski as agent for Boguski. For text of this patent see Appendix B.

[21] E.S. & A. Co. *vs.* P.R. Co., 1901 case, Complainant's Proofs, pp. 106 and 125.

[22] *Ibid.*, pp. 213-14.

[23] *Ibid.*, pp. 404-6.

[24] John B. C. Kershaw, *Electrometallurgy* (New York: D. Van Nostrand Co., 1908), p. 47.

[25] *Ibid.*, p. 101.

[26] Wallace, *op. cit.*, pp. 508-11.

[27] U.S. Patent Office hearing, Fauré *vs.* Cowles & Cowles *vs.* Bradley & Crocker, December 19, 1888, p. 162.

[28] Hartford, *op. cit.*, pp. 5-6. See also *Alfred Hutchinson Cowles—A Biographical Sketch,* National Cyclopedia of American Biography (New York: James T. White & Co., 1916), p. 6.

[29] Kershaw, *op. cit.*, pp. 224-25.

[30] J. N. Pring, *The Electric Furnace* (London: Longmans, Green & Co., 1921), p. 344.

[31] Edward G. Acheson, *Pathfinder, Discovery, Invention, Industry* (New York: Press Scrap Book, 1910), pp. 109-22.

[32] C.C.W.D., Pa., 1897, 83 Fed. 492.

[33] Cowles Electric Smelting & Aluminum Co. *vs.* Carborundum Co., C.C.W.D., Pa., 1897, Complainant's Proofs, pp. 255-61, 289-95, 577-78 (decision reported 83 Fed. 492).

[34] *Ibid.*

[35] The *Encyclopaedia Britannica*, 1953 ed., XX, 656, states that Acheson accidentally discovered silicon carbide in 1871. He was born March 6, 1856, so that he would have been 15 years of age in 1871. The statement that he discovered it is incorrect and the date given is 20 years earlier than that reported by Acheson as the date of his alleged discovery.

[36] C.C.W.D., Pa., 1897, 83 Fed. 492.

[37] C.C.A. 3rd, Pa., 1900, 102 Fed. 618.

[38] C.C.W.D., Pa., 1900, 189 Fed. 710.

[39] C.C.A. 3rd, Pa., 1913, 203 Fed. 976.

[40] National Cyclopedia of American Biography, *Alfred Hutchinson Cowles—A Biographical Sketch* (New York: James T. White & Co., 1916), p. 5.

[41] Acheson, *op. cit.*, pp. 109-22.

[42] Wallace, *op. cit.*, p. 521.

[43] Wallace, *op. cit.*, p. 526.

Chapter V

Charles Schenck Bradley

The Cowles brothers had one rival for priority in conception of the electric-furnace idea. This was Charles Schenck Bradley, born in Victor, New York, on April 12, 1853, who attended school at DeGraff Military Institute in Rochester, New York, subsequently spending some time in 1872 at the University of Rochester. Bradley went to work for Edison in New York as an engineer in 1881. From 1883 to 1914 he was successively employed by various electric companies and, from 1916 on, by the U.S. Reduction Company. In addition to his patents covering the decomposition of ores by electricity, he also took out patents for an improved electric generator, three-phase transmission of power, and fixation of atmospheric nitrogen.

Hammond in his history of the General Electric Company reports that during the early 1890's Bradley in his laboratory at Yonkers, New York, developed a rotary or synchronous converter, with a revolving field and stationary armature, which received alternating current at one end and by means of a commutator delivered it as direct current at the other end.[1] This made it possible for trolley lines which always used direct current, and the direct current lighting lines already in existence, to be incorporated in unified systems employing alternating current. Bradley established in 1893 at Yonkers a factory operated by the Bradley Electric Power Company for the manufacture of these converters, but this was taken over before long by the General Electric Company. He died in 1929 at the age of 76.[2]

In the spring of 1885 the Cowles brothers were planning substantial expenditures in establishing their plant at Lockport, New York, for the commercial production of aluminum and its alloys.[3] Bradley at that point entered the scene for the first time as a result of the Cowles brothers receiving notice from the United States Patent Office of an interference between their patent application and Bradley's in which one of his attorneys, Francis B. Crocker, was a joint inventor. Under established Patent Office procedure they were not advised as to details of the Bradley and Crocker invention, the date on which the application was filed, or any experimental work which might have preceded the filing. The Cowles brothers were thus in the highly precarious position of being threatened with loss of their patent rights and of being unable to find out how serious the threat might be. Therefore, they immediately communicated with Bradley and Crocker and arranged to buy for $5000 all of their inventions which were in conflict in the Patent Office with Cowles inventions.[4] Prior to making this purchase they did not know that an earlier Bradley application was also pending or that it would ultimately prove to be by far the more important of the two.[5]

After having acquired the Bradley and Crocker inventions sight unseen the Cowles brothers arranged for a referee to determine priority between the rival patent applications. For this purpose they selected General M. D. Leggett, formerly United States Commissioner of Patents, who ascertained the facts from both groups with the result that Bradley and Crocker conceded priority on most points to the Cowles brothers. The decision of the referee in this case should presumably be interpreted as limited in scope because his attention had been focused on the March 14, 1885, application of Bradley and Crocker.[6] This was due to the fact that Bradley's February 23, 1883, application had lain dormant for more than two years, rejected by the Patent Office because of the early work of Sir Humphry Davy. General Leggett, however, must have been aware of Bradley's previous work because the Bradley and Crocker patent, application for which he had under consideration, contained the following statement:

In an application of Letters Patent of the United States now pending (filed February 23, 1883, Serial No. 85,957) Charles S. Bradley, one of the present inventors, has described an electrometallurgical process in which an electric current is employed to perform two functions: first, to effect the electrolytic decomposition of the materials treated, and, second, to supply the heat necessary to maintain said materials in the fused state while they are being electrolyzed.

The earlier Bradley patent application, filed on February 23, 1883, was divided into three in 1887, and about the end of 1889 Bradley granted an option on these to Lowrey, the Western Union patent attorney who organized the Edison Company. The sale of this option to Lowrey was undoubtedly a legitimate transaction on the part of Bradley. Lowrey, an experienced patent lawyer who could hardly have been unaware of all the circumstances, was apparently proceeding in the hope that he might be able to prove that the Cowles Company had purchased only the patent rights of Bradley involved in formal patent office interference rather than all the ideas covered by him which might interfere in a broader sense. When two of these Bradley patents were finally issued in the winter of 1891-1892 litigation between Lowrey and the Cowles Company ensued for the purpose of determining their ownership.[7] Judge William Howard Taft on April 23, 1895, rendered a decision against the Cowles Company.[8] This was reversed by the higher court in a decision handed down by Judge Severens on February 15, 1897, thereby establishing the Cowles Company as owner of the Bradley patents.[9]

The most illuminating information as to priority in conceiving the electric-furnace idea is to be found in the record of a three-way Patent Office interference proceeding near the end of 1888 among the patent applications of the Cowles brothers, Bradley and Crocker, and Camille A. Fauré, a Frenchman, living in New York, who had developed a process for the production of aluminum chloride in an electric arc furnace. It was only because of Fauré's involvement that these interference proceedings occurred because prior to that time the Cowles brothers had bought the Bradley and Crocker application and so, under Patent Office rules, were not entitled to an adjudication by the Patent Office of priority between their two patent applications. This interference produced the only contest in which the early work of Bradley and the Cowles brothers was the subject of sworn testimony. The testimony of Bradley and Crocker did not carry back the priority of their invention to any date early enough to be of significance and, as the cross-examination of them both shows, no effort was made in this direction, presumably because there had already been a concession of priority to the Cowles brothers.[10]

Eugene Cowles testified that in 1880 he was working on the idea of an electric furnace and that he made a sketch of a furnace which he showed to his father and others on September 1 of that year.[11] He stated that in 1880 he was entirely familiar with the difference between arc and incandescent electric heating, that he had at that time discussed with his brother both types of furnace, and that the sketch which he showed his father depicted a type which could be operated either as an arc or incandescent furnace. His testimony indicated that conception of his electric-furnace idea occurred on or about September 1, 1880, although it was not reduced to actual practice until he conducted the experiments in Cleveland during May of 1884.

Alfred H. Cowles testified that while a student at Cornell University (he was there from the fall of 1877 to June, 1882) he performed an experiment, basic to his electric-furnace concept, which measured the amount of heat that a given quantity of electricity would generate in passing through a continuous conductor offering a given resistance.[12] Such information was not available to an undergraduate of 75 to 80 years ago in convenient handbook form as it is today. The Cowles brothers stated that from 1880 on they were intermittently preoccupied with the electric-furnace problem for several years. They introduced as evidence an actual drawing, made by them in June, 1883, at Santa Fe, which depicted an incandescent electric furnace embodying the same principles as that used today in the aluminum industry, and both brothers testified that throughout the latter part of 1882 they were working on the electric-furnace idea and that in the winter of 1882-1883 they had made sketches depicting such a furnace which they had shown to several witnesses but had not preserved. There can be no doubt that their conception of the electric-furnace idea antedated the filing of Bradley's patent application on February 23, 1883, and there is no information available as to how long prior to the filing date Bradley developed the ideas embodied in his patent. It may have been, as frequently happens, that the concept was first crystallized at a conference in his patent lawyer's office and that preparation and filing of the patent application followed immediately. Or perhaps Bradley, like the Cowles brothers, had been thinking and making sketches for some time prior to the filing of his application. At least it is clear from the evidence that

Bradley, prior to filing his application, had not constructed an apparatus and demonstrated his process.[13]

The Cowles brothers received extensive recognition during their lives for development of the electric furnace and Charles Martin Hall was also greatly honored for his part in originating the commercial process for making aluminum. Nevertheless, in the litigation which arose over ownership of this valuable invention, it was neither the Cowles brothers nor Hall who received primary credit in the last round of the protracted courtroom encounters. In the final court battle between the Cowles Company and the Pittsburgh Reduction Company, victory, it is true, was won by the Cowles Company, but as owner of an invention by the comparatively obscure Bradley. This raises the question as to why the Cowles interests elected to bring suit against Hall's Pittsburgh Reduction Company for infringement, not of their own patent, but of a patent issued to Bradley.

In order to clarify the situation with respect to priority between Bradley and the Cowles brothers it is necessary at this point to digress briefly in order to explain a certain oddity in the law defining priority in which a distinction is made between determining to whom a patent shall be issued and determining the validity of a patent which has already been issued. From the legal viewpoint there are three important dates in the development of a patentable idea, (1) when the idea was first conceived by the inventor, (2) when the inventor first reduced it to practice, that is, when he first constructed an apparatus and successfully demonstrated his idea, and (3) when he filed the application for his patent. The Patent Office, in determining priority for the purpose of issuing a patent, considers only the date on which the application was filed unless the idea was reduced to practice prior to filing. In the latter case the date of reduction to practice becomes the significant one unless the inventor can prove that, after conceiving his idea, he exercised due diligence in reducing it to practice, in which case the date on which he conceived the idea becomes the significant one. An inventor may be held to have exercised "due diligence" even though an appreciable lapse of time has occurred between the conception of his idea and reducing it to practice, provided the reason for the delay was beyond his control. Such a reason might be illness, temporary lack of funds needed to acquire the necessary apparatus or perhaps, in the case of the Cowles brothers, enforced absence for health reasons in the wilds of New Mexico where it was impossible to procure the necessary equipment and electric power.

The case just discussed, where the Patent Office is deciding the issue of priority between rival applicants for a patent, is different in one important respect from the case in which a patent, after issue, is defended against the assertion that it is invalid because of prior invention by someone other than the patentee. The patent, once issued, carries the legal presumption that it is valid. In order to invalidate it by showing prior invention by someone else a very strict standard of proof must be observed to show beyond any reasonable doubt that the alleged prior invention was in fact made before invention by the patentee. As a practical matter, this means that someone other than the patentee must have reduced the invention to practice at a date earlier than that which can be sustained by the patentee. The mere showing that someone else had the idea in mind, or discussed it, or disclosed it to others, even if this be shown conclusively, is not sufficient. In a decision where this kind of issue was under adjudication, Judge Learned Hand said in his opinion:

Mere acquaintance with the invention, even if disclosed, is not enough; nothing short of "reduction to practice" will do, whatever that may mean. . . . All this is very old law, though it is by no means always easy to ascertain just when "reduction" has taken place, for the books, perhaps wisely, are reticent of positive definition . . . in such cases probability, even extreme probability, is not enough.[14]

Because of the difference between the attitude of the courts with respect to an issued patent and the established procedure under which the Patent Office determines priority between rival inventors, it is possible that the Cowles brothers might have been able to establish their priority over Bradley if the Patent Office had had the occasion to determine this question. Such evidence, however, showing the reduction to practice by the Cowles brothers in Cleveland, following their return from New Mexico where it would have been impossible to construct and prove the utility of the electric furnace, would not have constituted adequate grounds for invalidating the Bradley patent when it became the subject of an infringement suit.

It is thus quite possible that the Cowles brothers conceived the idea prior to Bradley and that they could have sustained their priority in a Patent Office contest with him. Such a contest never occurred due to the fact that the Cowles brothers' attorney, while making their patent application, acquiesced in relinquishing the broad claims which Lowrey later obtained for the Bradley patent through Patent Office appeal procedures. The fact that the Cowles brothers at an earlier stage of the proceedings might have been able to win a Patent Office contest with Bradley had no bearing on their ability to assert the Bradley patent, when later they owned it, with the certainty, under established law, that their own early work did not render the Bradley patent invalid.

A point worth mentioning is that Bradley's attorney, Crocker, admitted under cross-examination in the contest between Lowrey and the Cowles Company over ownership of the Bradley patents that he did not know of any instance in which an apparatus had actually been constructed and Bradley's process demonstrated.[15] Also the court which finally adjudicated the Bradley patent accepted as true the characterization of it as a "paper patent," that is, one which had not been reduced to practice.[16] The court quite rightly concluded, however, that it did not matter whether Bradley had ever demonstrated his invention so long as the patent itself disclosed a working embodiment of his idea. In view of these facts it seems to be well established that the Cowles brothers put their electric furnace into successful operation and began commercial production with it before Bradley ever made his apparatus, if indeed he ever did make any apparatus. It is equally clear that Bradley filed a patent application describing an electric furnace before the Cowles brothers reduced their idea to practice, but that they conceived their idea before Bradley filed his application.

There is one further important point which made the Bradley patent preferable to the Cowles patent as a basis for court action. The Cowles brothers' application originally asked for patent claims as broad as those embodied in the Bradley patent and covering just as adequately the process used by the Pittsburgh Reduction Company. Certain of the Cowles claims, however, were rejected by the Patent Office because of work done by Sir Humphry Davy who in the period from 1807 to 1809 had employed batteries to produce small amounts of aluminum alloy, as well as some other metals, by electrolytically separating them from the solutions of their salts. The attorneys for the Cowles brothers apparently acquiesced in this ruling by the Patent Examiner and cancelled these broad claims of their clients. The important concept of electrolysis was thus abandoned. This is indicated by various changes in wording between the original application and the patent as finally issued. Noteworthy among these is the fact that in the Cowles patent appeared the following clause not included in the original application, "and we are aware that an electric current has been employed in the reduction of fused ores, and we do not claim the same broadly." This presumably was a reference to Davy's electrolytic experiments at the beginning of the century. In the case of the Bradley application similar claims were originally rejected by the Patent Office for the same reason.

The 1883 Bradley application, however, was kept alive for nine years through attempts to overcome the Davy reference. This was done chiefly through the efforts of Grosvenor P. Lowrey, the New York patent lawyer who was the United States representative of Héroult and other European aluminum interests. According to Albert Stetson, a New York electrical engineer and patent expert, Lowrey, in the latter part of 1889 or the beginning of 1890, paid Bradley $1000 for an option to acquire his 1883 inventions.[17] Lowrey about 1896 negotiated sale of these to certain European interests for $50,000, of which he claimed that he was to get $37,500 and Bradley $12,500. The deal fell through, however, because Bradley refused to transfer his interests in these patents to the European buyers on the ground that he, and not Lowrey, was entitled to $37,500 of the $50,000 purchase price. Bradley never assigned his patents to anyone entitled to them under Lowrey's option, and could not have been induced to do so, according to Stetson, except through a lawsuit which was never undertaken. Lowrey's negotiations for sale of the Bradley patents to the European interests took place after the decision of the Cowles-Lowrey case in which the Circuit Court in April, 1895, awarded to Lowrey title to the Bradley patents, but before the Circuit Court of Appeals in February, 1897, reversed this decision and awarded title to the Cowles Company. Lowrey died before the date of this latter decision.[18]

During the period in which Lowrey held the option on the Bradley 1883 inventions he appealed the case and through energetic action got the Patent Office examiner's rejection overruled, thus obtaining in 1892 the grant of broad claims which the Cowles brothers' attorneys had abandoned. It was at this point that Lowrey initiated his unsuccessful litigation with the Cowles Company which in 1897 resulted in establishing Cowles ownership of the Bradley patents. Since the Cowles patent expired on June 9, 1902, whereas Bradley's most important patent did not expire until February 2, 1909, and since the Bradley patent carried broader claims, these constituted added reasons why the Bradley patent was more desirable than the Cowles patent as the basis for an infringement suit.

In view of the fact that there was never a Patent Office adjudication of priority between Bradley and the Cowles brothers the best that can be done here is to examine what evidence is available, at the same time recognizing that the story is too incomplete for a sure conclusion to be possible. Some light was thrown on the matter by United States Commissioner of Patents James T. Newton at a meeting of the American Electrochemical Society in April, 1927.[19] He confirmed the fact that, while there had never been any Patent Office determination of priority between Bradley and the Cowles brothers patent applications as to the broader claims, yet on the narrower issues, where Patent Office interferences had existed, Bradley himself had either conceded priority to the Cowles brothers or had been defeated by them in interference proceedings. Commissioner Newton concluded with the statement that his careful investigations into the early history of aluminum disclosed that the Cowles brothers were the first to apply the electric furnace (experimentally) in the production of aluminum by electrolysis in a bath maintained in a fused condition by electric current.

The evidence indicates that not even the Cowles brothers themselves ever knew whether they or Bradley were first in conceiving the electric-furnace idea which became an essential part of the modern aluminum industry. On the witness stand in 1895 Alfred H. Cowles stated that he did not know the answer to the cross-question as to whether the invention of the Bradley patent was prior to the date of the invention of the Cowles patent.[20] In amplification of this statement he further testified, "Off the record you have explained that by the expression 'the invention of the Bradley patents,' you do not mean the date of application but the date of invention. I do not know Bradley's date of invention, nor do I know what the courts would construe to be our date of invention on the issue that might exist between us and Bradley."

One thing is sure, however, that among the five, Hall, Héroult, Bradley, and the Cowles brothers, the Cowles brothers were the first to place in operation an electric furnace which could be used commercially and which was used as early as 1884 to produce aluminum alloy at one-third of the cost of producing it by any other method then known. It is also true that introduction of the modern process by the Cowles Company and the Pittsburgh Reduction Company reduced the price of pure aluminum in 1891 to 50 cents a pound, which was 3.3 per cent of its 1884 level. This great advance could not have been accomplished by them at that time without employing the Cowles electric furnace because it was not until almost a year later that details of the Bradley invention became known to them through issue of his patent. In fact, the widely-publicized achievements of the Cowles brothers with their electric furnace, beginning in 1884 and culminating with the sensational reduction in the price of aluminum in 1890 and 1891, were what provided the incentive for Lowrey to purchase an option on the Bradley application and undertake the patent office appeal procedures which resulted in issue of the patent in 1892.

NOTES

[1] Hammond, *op. cit.*, pp. 230-31.

[2] *Who Was Who in America, 1897-1942* (Chicago: A. N. Marquis Co., 1942).

[3] In the beginning the Lockport plant was employed only in the production of aluminum alloys. Ever since 1884, however, the Cowles brothers had been experimenting with the objective of developing a commercial process for the manufacture of aluminum. At the end of 1890 they began production of the pure metal which resulted in protracted patent litigation.

[4] U.S. Patent Office hearing, Fauré *vs.* Cowles & Cowles *vs.* Bradley & Crocker, November 19, 1888, p. 50.

[5] U.S. Patent No. 468,148, issued February 2, 1892, original application filed February 23, 1883.

[6] U.S. Patent No. 335,499, issued February 2, 1886.

[7] U.S. Patent No. 464,933, was issued December 8, 1891, and No. 468,148, on February 2, 1892.

[8] C.C.N.D. Ohio, E.D., 1895, 68 Fed. 354.

[9] C.C.A. 6th, Ohio, 1897, 79 Fed. 331.

[10] U.S. Patent Office hearing, Fauré *vs.* Cowles & Cowles *vs.* Bradley & Crocker, November 18, 1888, pp. 5-51.

[11] *Ibid.*, January 21, 1889, pp. 367-87.

[12] *Ibid.*, December 19, 1888, p. 155.

[13] See pp. 58-59.

[14] Block *vs.* Nathan Anklet Support Co., C.C.A. 2nd, 1925, 9 Fed. 2nd 311 at 313.

[15] Lowrey *vs.* Cowles Electric Smelting & Aluminum Co., C.C.N.D., Ohio, 1895, Complainant's Proofs, p. 21 (decision reported 68 Fed. 354).

[16] Pittsburgh Reduction Co. *vs.* Cowles Electric Smelting and Aluminum Co., C.C.A. 2nd, New York, 1903, 125 Fed. 926. See also Edwards, Frary, and Jeffries, *op. cit.*, I, 30.

[17] E.S. & A. Co. *vs.* P.R. Co., 1901 case, Complainant's Proofs, pp. 1069 and 1074.

[18] *Ibid.*, p. 6.

[19] Hartford, *op. cit.*, pp. 10-13.

[20] Cowles Electric Smelting and Aluminum Co. *vs.* Carborundum Co., C.C.W.D., Pa., 1897, Complainant's Proofs, pp. 101-2 (decision reported 83 Fed. 492).

Chapter VI

Charles Martin Hall

While Bradley and the Cowles brothers had conceived the idea of the electric furnace in the period from 1880 to 1883, and while the Cowles brothers had successfully operated the electric furnace in 1884 and had actually established a plant for producing aluminum alloys during 1885, the modern process for extracting pure aluminum was not complete until the idea was developed of reducing it by electrolysis of alumina dissolved in molten cryolite. This is the step attributed to Paul L. T. Héroult of France and Charles Martin Hall in the United States who, independently of each other and almost simultaneously, made proposals along these lines. Hall's United States patent application was filed on July 9, 1886, seven weeks after Héroult's United States application which was filed on May 22 of that year. Witnesses, however, testified that on February 23, 1886, while experimenting in his family's woodshed at Oberlin, Ohio, Hall made the discovery upon which his application was based.[1] There seems to be some doubt as to whether, under then-existing United States patent law, Héroult was permitted to carry back the date of his invention to April 23, 1886, when the certificate for his French patent was issued,[2] or only to May 22 of that year, the date on which his United States application was filed. This question is irrelevant since both of these events were preceded by the February 23, 1886, date established by Hall. Under our Patent Office regulations a citizen of this country is given certain advantages over a foreigner. Hall, for example, was granted priority because of being able to prove that he had demonstrated his process before Héroult filed his application, and in spite of the fact that Héroult was first in applying for a United States Patent and may also have preceded Hall in conceiving and demonstrating the idea.

Actually, Hall deserves equal credit because he developed the process independently of Héroult. Both men, however, originally intended that the bath was to be heated by external fire and, thus, they were faced with the unavoidable deficiencies of external heating so that, while their idea as to the type of bath in which to accomplish electrolysis of the alumina later proved to be essential, it was quite impractical for commercial use as applied in the beginning by both of these inventors.

Hall was born in 1863 at Thompson, Ohio, where his father, the Reverend Heman B. Hall, was pastor of a Congregational church. The family later moved to Oberlin, Ohio, and Hall graduated in 1885 from Oberlin College. While there his attention was directed to aluminum in the chemistry courses of Professor Frank F. Jewett, Yale 1870, who had studied in Germany under Professor Friedrich Wöhler, by then over 70 years of age but still one of the world's greatest authorities on aluminum.

The Cowles brothers first met Hall in the latter part of July, 1887, when he was visiting his uncle, Dr. M. L. Brooks, who was their family physician in Cleveland and a stockholder in the Cowles Electric Smelting and Aluminum Company. An arrangement was made whereby Hall was provided with equipment and various services, and was paid a monthly salary, while demonstrating at the Cowles works in Lockport, New York, his process for extracting aluminum, the Cowles Electric Smelting and Aluminum Company having taken an option whereby it might acquire his patent applications in exchange for one-eighth of the Cowles Company stock.[3]

The Cowles brothers near the end of June, 1887, a month before they first met Hall, had received from their London agent the drawings and specification for Héroult's patent [4] covering the idea of electrolyzing alumina dissolved in cryolite fused with external heat, and five months before that they had purchased Boguski's patents, the most important of which they had first examined in July, 1886,[5] concluding that it might cover this same general concept. It is clear, therefore, that the Cowles brothers had heard of this process before their first meeting with Hall in the latter half of July, 1887. Hall's first patent, applied for a year before, had not as yet been issued and there was some doubt as to whether the ideas which formed the basis for it would not turn out to have been anticipated by prior inventors, thereby invalidating the Hall patent. In fact, when the Cowles brothers first met Hall they were under the impression that the idea of electrolyzing alumina dissolved in cryolite was old in the art and, therefore, not patentable.[6] They had a copy of a British patent, issued in 1861 to Thomas Bell as agent for Louis Le Chatelier of Paris, a co-worker with Deville, which described a process in which aluminum was plated onto metal surfaces by electrolysis employing various alternative baths, among them cryolite, which had been fused by external combustion heat.[7] Anodes composed of alumina and carbon were immersed in this bath. The alumina in the anodes would, of course, dissolve upon contact with the molten cryolite. The Cowles brothers also had a copy of an 1883 French patent of an invention by Julien Edward Varin which proposed a soluble anode process very similar to that of Le Chatelier.[8] Varin's anodes were composed of 90 per cent alumina and 10 per cent carbon. His specification of various alternative baths included double fluoride of aluminum and sodium (cryolite) which would dissolve the alumina in the anodes. When pure aluminum was to be produced he recommended cathodes consisting of coarsely flattened sheets of aluminum on which would be deposited by electrolysis thick layers of additional aluminum, the sheets composing the cathodes and the deposits thereon being subsequently melted down into aluminum ingots. Another item in the Cowles brothers' collection was a British patent representing an idea transmitted in 1884 by Dr. Richard Grätzel of Hanover, Germany, which described the production of aluminum by electrolysis, employing soluble anodes and baths in terms which the Cowles brothers considered broad enough to cover the dissolving of alumina in molten cryolite.[9] They also believed that Boguski's 1884 British patent, which they had purchased six months before together with his United States rights, was the first to propose the electrolysis of a solution in which simple alumina, as distinct from soluble anodes containing alumina, was added to a cryolite bath and that, if anyone was entitled to a patent on this idea it was Boguski. The United States Patent Office, however, had rejected his application because of the work of earlier inventors.

Hall's original July 9, 1886, patent application covering the employment of a cryolite bath had been divided and a second application filed on February 2, 1887, the central idea of which was "dissolving alumina in a fused bath composed of the fluorides of aluminum and potassium, and then passing an electric current by means of an anode formed of non-carbonaceous material, through the fused mass. . . ." [10] The above quotation is from the last patent application filed by Hall before his arrival at Lockport in July, 1887. It describes the process which he was advocating while there. The Cowles brothers thought that Hall, in this second patent application might have an improvement upon his first idea, namely, a bath which melted at a temperature enough lower than cryolite to permit fusing it with external combustion heat which Hall claimed would be more economical than internal electric heat. They were influenced to a large extent by this consideration in their decision to give Hall advice and facilities to experiment in their plant for a year, and also to help him with his interference contest in the United States Patent Office.

While the Patent Examiner had declared an interference to exist between Hall and Héroult which was broad enough to cover electrolysis of alumina dissolved in cryolite, the Cowles brothers doubted at the time that such a claim would be allowed without reference to the mechanical and electrical means required for the successful operation of the process. They thought it probable that neither they, through ownership of Boguski's United States rights, nor Hall, nor Héroult could establish a valid claim on so broad a basis. Héroult's claims were, however, thought to be broad enough to cover, not only Hall's first patent application, but also his second one. At that time the Cowles brothers were primarily interested in doing what they could to prevent Hall's second application from being disallowed but, since they held an option on all of his patent rights, they naturally wished to protect any other of these which might turn out to be at stake in the interference with Héroult. Alfred H. Cowles testified that he was individually responsible for employing the firm of Leggett and Leggett to do the work necessary for Hall's protection in that case.[11] If the Cowles brothers had not loaned Hall the services of their patent lawyers he might have been defeated by Héroult, thus losing not only the rights involved in his second patent application but also those represented by his first application which ultimately turned out to be the important one.

When Hall first met the Cowles brothers in the latter part of July, 1887, they had actually been experimenting for some time with the modern process for producing aluminum, namely, electrolyzing alumina dissolved in cryolite fused by internal electric heat. Alfred H. Cowles later testified that he and his brother knew about cryolite by the end of 1884 or early in 1885 and that during the last half of 1886 they had discussed rendering alumina fusible at a lower temperature through employment of a suitable flux. This was when they were considering the purchase of Boguski's patent.[12] Early in 1887, stimulated in part by rumors of Héroult's activities in Europe, they decided to start working intensively on the problem of producing pure aluminum. At that time they began to experiment with dissolving alumina in cryolite.[13] On June 10, 1887, Eugene Cowles wrote to Ben M. Plumb, their London agent, that they had been prevented up to then from producing pure aluminum by the lack of pure ore, but that they hoped within a week to be able to send him a malleable brick of relatively pure aluminum, made by their process, which would contain only about one-half of 1 per cent silicon.[14] Correspondence between the Cowles Lockport plant and their Cleveland office, dated June 7 and 18, 1887, indicated that they had substantial amounts of cryolite on hand in Lockport at that time [15] and on June 16, 1887, their analytical chemist, H. N. Yates, reported on an experiment with cryolite and corundum in which 30 pounds of metal was produced, no information being given as to the amount of impurities contained therein.[16] On July 9, 1887, Romaine Cole, the Cowles general manager, wrote a letter to the Pennsylvania Salt Company ordering 200 pounds of cryolite and 200 pounds of alumina to be used in a continuation of these experiments,[17] and on July 6 of that year he wrote to a man in South Pueblo, Colorado, in connection with a Colorado cryolite deposit, requesting samples, and asking who owned it and whether it was for sale.[18]

The results of the Cowles brothers' experiments with the modern aluminum process in the spring and early summer of 1887 had up to that point been unsatisfactory, probably due to the fact that they were using corundum, a native alumina containing impurities, mainly iron and silicon, which resulted in the production of alloys instead of pure aluminum. Hall told them at that time that he had conducted extensive experiments with alumina and cryolite, the very combination that ultimately proved successful, that this approach was no good, but that he had developed something better, namely, the bath with a lower melting point than cryolite which he thought, therefore, could be used with external heat and the copper anodes which he was then attempting to employ.[19] On the strength of Hall's representations the Cowles brothers abandoned for the time being their experiments with alumina dissolved in cryolite and instead spent a year in fruitless backing of Hall's unsuccessful attempts to develop his idea of employing copper anodes to electrolyze alumina dissolved in a bath fused by external heat. The bath being advocated by Hall at that time, a double fluoride of aluminum and potassium, was quite different from cryolite which is a double fluoride of aluminum and sodium. The record is not clear as to just when Hall switched back to cryolite, but he did not abandon copper anodes until September, 1888, and external heating until January, 1889.

In the summer of 1887, and for 18 months thereafter, Hall was thwarted by the fact that his crucibles, if large enough to be commercially practicable, were quickly destroyed, in part by the external combustion heat which he was using to fuse the bath, and in part by the corrosive effect of the bath itself. Shortly after first meeting Hall the Cowles brothers had suggested to him that this problem might be overcome by using internal electric heat instead of external combustion heat, and by employing thicker carbon linings for the crucibles instead of the thin ones which he was compelled to use in order to admit the external heat. The thicker carbon linings would serve the double purpose of preventing escape of the internal electric heat and of better protecting the walls of the crucibles from the corrosive effect of the bath. The Cowles brothers also explained to Hall that it would be necessary to adjust the current to meet requirements for fusing and electrolysis in a crucible of definite size. They pointed out, however, that in employing internal electric heat he would be adopting an idea then thought to be original with them. They were referring to their first patent [20] covering the electric-furnace concept which had been applied for on December 23, 1884, a year and a half before Hall's application, and had been issued June 9, 1885, eight months before the date on which Hall made his woodshed experiment.

Hall, while at Lockport during 1887 and 1888, did not adopt the Cowles brothers' suggestion that he employ internal electric heat. In fact, he could not have done so while continuing to use the bath and anodes which he was then advocating. At that time he seemed to attribute major importance to certain features of his apparatus. In seeking to interest the Cowles brothers he claimed to have discovered, for example, that it was possible to employ his copper anodes instead of carbon anodes which the Cowles brothers had been using and which, incidentally, are still used to this day.

The carbon anodes were gradually consumed or burned in the process because of the liberation of oxygen on their surfaces under high temperature conditions. One of Hall's arguments in favor of copper anodes was that they would not be consumed. His idea was that, as oxygen was liberated, a copper oxide layer would be formed on the surface of the anode which would prevent further attack on the metal. Due to his use of these anodes he was forced to employ external heat because, as he admitted on the witness stand 12 years later, "It is impossible to use a copper anode for carrying out fusion with an electric current without immediately melting down the copper anode and spoiling not only it, but the bath, by contamination with copper." [21] In 1887 he assured the Cowles brothers that the use of external heat would be practicable because the bath he was then using, fluorides of aluminum and potassium, could be fused at well below the melting point of pure cryolite, thus avoiding the difficulties caused by applying intense heat externally. Later he abandoned this bath in favor of various other mixtures which usually included cryolite, but also as necessary ingredients certain other salts such as common sodium chloride and the fluorides of aluminum, lithium, potassium, or calcium.[22]

In the patent litigation 12 years after he went to Lockport, Hall admitted under cross-examination the impracticability of the version of his process in which during 1887 he had sought to interest the Cowles brothers. In answer to a question as to whether he had disclosed that the use of copper anodes would prevent using the current to fuse the bath, Hall testified that he was using copper anodes at that time and that obviously this would have prevented using the current to fuse the bath. He further stated that carbon anodes would have spoiled the bath used at that time.[23] In reply to a question as to how the use of carbon anodes spoiled the bath Hall testified:

The bath was a double fluoride of aluminum and potassium. When a carbon anode is used for heating and electrolyzing this, no aluminum is produced, or only a very small quantity. The bath also becomes changed in its chemical composition in some way which I do not understand yet. From being thin and very liquid, it becomes thick and mushy and full of some black substance, and also froths up in a very remarkable way. I found that with this bath, as I was working it then, it was necessary to use anodes containing no carbon.[24]

That Hall had experienced difficulties at Lockport with external heating is indicated by a letter which he wrote on August 2, 1888, to the Cowles Electric Smelting and Aluminum Company, shortly after he had left Lockport, in reply to an inquiry from them as to the correctness of a bill which they were about to pay for various items of equipment furnished to him while there. In this letter Hall said,

The patterns charged were all made and I know that there was a considerable amount of work on them and subsequent alterations in them. The bill is about what I supposed it would be. The crucibles charged all proved leaky on short use but from my experience I think it rather difficult to secure cast iron crucibles that would answer any better under the same conditions.

Dudley Baldwin, who in July, 1887, replaced Cole as the Cowles general manager, reported that, while at Lockport, Hall was using very small crucibles.[25] In the beginning these were wrought-iron cylinders, ordinarily used as containers for mercury, 11 inches high and five inches in diameter. Later he used cast iron pots 18 inches high and eight inches in diameter, but these were quickly destroyed. Alfred H. Cowles testified that Hall in his experiments at Lockport had reached the limit to which the process he was then employing could go as to size of crucible.[26] Cowles explained that with external fire it was found impossible to use a large crucible for Hall's operations for the reason that, if the diameter of the crucible be doubled, its capacity increases fourfold. Hence, to fuse the contents, four times the quantity of heat must pass through the walls of the crucible, and yet these walls, to be of adequate strength, had to be made thicker as the size increased. It was found that, as the size of crucible was increased, a point was soon reached where the amount of external heat needed to fuse the contents would destroy the walls. It was this difficulty which forced Hall to adopt the Cowles electric furnace in 1889, because he found that with external heat to fuse the bath he could not operate on a scale large enough to be practicable from the commercial viewpoint.

Various Alcoa (Aluminum Company of America) historians have undertaken to explain Hall's impracticable use of external heat to fuse the bath during the three years from 1886 to 1889 by the argument that his early experiments had to be conducted on too small a scale to permit fusing by internal electric heat.[27] The implication has been that he had to operate on a miniature scale because of the necessity for economizing but, in view of the very modest requirements for equipment needed to demonstrate the modern commercial process with internal heat, it seems probable that Hall's small scale of operation was necessitated by some consideration other than the need for economy. For example, one cast-iron, carbon-lined pot, two feet long, 16 inches wide, and 20 inches high, will suffice, as evidenced by the fact that the Pittsburgh Reduction Company used pots of this size throughout the first year or more of its commercial operations,[28] after the first two months of which it was employing internal electric current, both for electrolysis and to fuse the bath, having discontinued entirely the use of external heat around the crucibles. If cryolite had been used as a bath the cost of it and the alumina required for an experimental run in a pot of that size would have been less than $10.[29]

Throughout Hall's year at Lockport the Cowles plant there was being continuously operated for the production of aluminum alloys, employing pots and electric current which were adequate in scale to have permitted operation of the modern process for the production of pure aluminum. If Hall at that time had believed and stated that the only thing preventing the functioning of his process was the scale of operations, it is unthinkable that the Cowles brothers, who were paying him a salary, as well as financing his patent litigation and experiments, would not have loaned him a little equipment and would not have supplied the modest amount of raw materials and electric power which would have been adequate to permit a successful demonstration.

Hall's major problem during the three years preceding 1889 had been that the walls of his crucibles tended to be destroyed by the external combustion heat employed to fuse the contents. He was compelled to use small crucibles because this difficulty became greater with any increase in size of the crucible. It was this trouble which also led him to employ the low-melting-point potassium-aluminum-fluoride bath which could not be used with carbon anodes, thus requiring that he resort to copper anodes. Once committed to copper anodes, he could not use internal electric heat because it melted the copper. These were the real reasons which compelled Hall to employ miniature crucibles and prevented his adopting internal electric heating. They had no connection with any need for economy.

Hall's first patent, applied for on July 9, 1886, was not issued until April, 1889, almost three years after the date of filing. During that period it was the subject of over 30 communications between Hall and the Patent Office and was rewritten several times. Various amendments were made, among them one on September 4, 1888, in which the copper anodes were abandoned. Commenting on these negotiations, Seabury Mastick, lecturer on chemical patents at Columbia University, said: "One of the peculiar things about the case is that although Hall made such a fight over his oxidized copper anodes, when his claims were finally formulated the only ones referring to anodes were for carbonaceous anodes, no written explanation appearing in the file for the sudden change." [30]

This statement by Mastick refers to Hall's first patent,[31] applied for on July 9, 1886, and not his second patent,[32] applied for on February 7, 1887, which as issued described a bath consisting of the fluorides of aluminum and potassium, copper anodes, and external heating. The features set forth in the second patent are the ones which Hall was advocating when he first met the Cowles brothers in the summer of 1887. When he later abandoned these ideas as unworkable he resorted to a modification of his earlier application which made specific mention of cryolite, but only as an item to be combined with other ingredients of the bath. This first patent described preparation of the bath for alumina as being preferably the fusing together of two salts in the proportions of 84 parts of sodium fluoride and 169 parts of aluminum fluoride. This is not simple cryolite, as indicated by Hall's further comments in which he said that a convenient method of forming his bath consisted of adding to the mineral cryolite 77.91 per cent of its weight of aluminum fluoride. With this addition the bath could be fused at a lower temperature than if it were composed only of cryolite and for this purpose Hall also suggested the substitution of fluoride of lithium for some of the sodium fluoride, thereby creating a combination containing 26 parts of lithium fluoride for every 126 parts of sodium fluoride and 338 parts of aluminum fluoride. Pure cryolite is 32.8 per cent sodium, 12.8 per cent aluminum, and 54.4 per cent fluorine,[33] or, to state it differently, 59.75 per cent sodium fluoride and 40.25 per cent aluminum fluoride.[34]

In his interference contest with Héroult in the United

States Patent Office Hall made the following comment on his woodshed experiment of February 23, 1886, in which he first reduced his invention to practice: "I took cryolite, which is a double fluoride of sodium and aluminum. To this I added a small quantity of aluminum fluoride. . . ."[35] This description of the bath in which the alumina was to be dissolved is not in agreement with the testimony of Hall's sister Julia or Professors Frank F. Jewett and Charles H. Churchill of Oberlin College, all of whom quoted Hall as stating that cryolite alone was used as a bath for the alumina. In view of the fact that Hall conducted the experiment in question, whereas the other "witnesses" were not present, it is probable that he was right and they wrong.

When Hall first went to Lockport in July, 1887, Edwin Cowles, president of the Cowles Company, wrote to Dudley Baldwin, its general manager, instructing him to provide Hall with all facilities needed to demonstrate his process. Alfred H. Cowles later testified that the Cowles Company provided Hall with all the equipment he asked for during his year at Lockport, in some cases having it made at local shops or in the Cowles foundry, and in other cases assigning their machinist, William Buckley, the task of working with Hall in designing and constructing his own apparatus.[36] Cowles further reported that their chemist, Theodore Stevens, was made available to Hall for consultation and to analyze his product.

In reply to the question as to what facilities there were at Lockport which Hall might have utilized, had he so desired, in employing internal heat to fuse his bath, Cowles replied that the Cowles works at Lockport and in England were the only two electric smelting plants existing in the world at that date, that they had at Lockport the largest dynamo and carbons in the world, and that their men knew how to handle this apparatus. He stated that Hall could not have secured anywhere else such advantageous facilities for fusing ore by internal electric heat as were placed at his disposal in Lockport when upon his arrival there the Cowles brothers suggested to him that he adopt this method of fusing.

Four months after Hall arrived in Lockport, Baldwin, the Cowles general manager, wrote to Edwin Cowles, "Hall is doing no good. I'm very tired of him. He made one good run of which I wrote you, but he can't duplicate it to save his life. He keeps no notes and says he has now forgotten or lost track of the process leading to the good result." During subsequent patent litigation, Baldwin testified, "I remember that Mr. Hall was extremely evasive and non-committal in answering any questions that I would put to him and consider pertinent, so that finally I concluded that if he was acting in good faith, his results were not successful." [37]

Alfred H. Cowles also testified [38] that during Hall's year at Lockport he made about 125 runs of his aluminum process, varying in duration from three to twelve hours, that in no one of these runs did he produce more than 10 or 12 ounces of aluminum, and that the metal produced was so full of impurities as to be only 90 to 93 per cent aluminum. Cowles further testified that Hall found it necessary to replace on practically every run the bath he was then using, that impurities in the aluminum came from the bath, and that these would have been eliminated if Hall had been successful in making his process continuous so far as the bath was concerned. The necessity for replacing the bath so frequently also added greatly to the expense of the process.

In later years Romaine C. Cole, promoter of the Pittsburgh Reduction Company, stated that Hall never made a sufficient quantity of aluminum at Lockport to make a satisfactory showing as to what his process could do, but that he had saved most of the buttons of metal which he had made during his year's work there.[39] Cole stated that in the summer of 1888 he and Hall melted these buttons into a large mass in order to interest and secure the financial support of a group in Pittsburgh, but he denied that they at that time claimed that the process was as yet a success.

One Alcoa writer, commenting on the Cowles failure to acquire the Hall patent, said, "It is difficult to understand why the Cowles Company passed up this golden opportunity." [40] While Hall was at Lockport for the 12 months ending July, 1888, the Cowles brothers were uncertain as to the outcome of his Patent Office contest. Obviously, also, they did not at that time appreciate the fact that one of Hall's patent applications covered a basic idea of such importance. It is only fair to emphasize, however, that he did not while at Lockport give a successful demonstration of his process. His troubles, originating with the employment of external heat and resulting in destruction of the crucibles, led to adoption of the unsatisfactory bath and anodes. Apparently Hall did not give up this unworkable process until after leaving Lockport in the summer of 1888, in September of that year abandoning the copper anodes in favor of carbon anodes and in January, 1889, replacing external combustion heat with internal electric heat, somewhere along the way having substituted a bath consisting mainly of cryolite for the unsatisfactory potassium-aluminum-fluoride bath. There is little resemblance between the modern process for producing aluminum and Hall's Lockport version which depended on copper anodes and external heat to fuse a bath consisting of the fluorides of aluminum and potassium. In view of the fact that Hall himself at that time still seemed unable to operate his process successfully, and even appeared to be under the impression that his worthless second patent application was the important one, it is not surprising that the Cowles brothers were so unfavorably impressed that they passed up the unquestionably "golden opportunity" of acquiring his patent rights.

When Hall first went to Lockport in July, 1887, the Cowles Company, in acquiring an option to purchase his patent applications, agreed to pay him a salary of $75 per month which in terms of 1957 wage levels was the equivalent of $500 to $600 per month. This salary was paid in full throughout the nine months during which three successive options were in effect, each for a period of three months.

Various Alcoa historians have published from time to time statements to the effect that the Cowles Company did not keep its agreement regarding certain payments allegedly due to Hall.[41] The first option gave the Cowles Company a 90-day period from July 27 to October 24, 1887, in which it had the privilege of acquiring Hall's patent rights in exchange for a one-eighth interest in the Cowles Company. The latter agreed to pay Hall $75 per month salary during this period and, in addition, an extra payment of $750 if, at the end of the three months, the Cowles people elected to keep the option in effect for an additional three months. Hall's demonstration of his process was so disappointing during the first three months that the Cowles Company decided against asserting its privilege of continuing the option for a longer period through payment of the $750 bonus to Hall. He was notified, therefore, that they had decided to let their original option expire at the end of the first three months. The Cowles Company agreed, however, to give Hall more time in which to work out a solution of his problems and he accordingly was permitted to use their plant and facilities for another three months under terms identical with those of the first option.[42] At the end of the second three-month period on January 26, 1888, the Cowles Company again permitted its option to expire, but agreed to a new three-month option on terms identical with those of the first two. Non-payment of the $750 bonus was the basis for claims that the Cowles Company did not keep its agreement. Apparently Hall and the Alcoa historians failed later to comprehend the distinction between the situation if the Cowles Company had exercised its right to keep the option in effect for a second three-month period, in which case an obligation to pay the bonus would have been incurred, and the true state of affairs in which the Cowles Company permitted its option to expire at the end of each successive three-month period, thus being under no obligation to pay the bonus.

Hall himself actually confirmed at the time the correctness of the position taken by the Cowles interests in this matter. On April 19, 1888, he wrote to A. T. Osborn, vice president of the Cowles Company, "As you probably know my contract with the company as renewed last February, requires the payment of $750 ninety days from January 24th, 1888, if the contract is to remain in force. This date comes on April 23. . . ." [43] It was on this latter date that the Cowles Company notified Hall that it was allowing its option on his process to lapse and Hall had clearly admitted in his letter to Osborn that under the circumstances the Cowles Company was not obligated to pay him the $750.

Another point on which the record needs to be set straight is that, however important the contribution of Hall and Héroult may have been, it is incorrect to say that either of them is entitled to credit for the discovery that alumina dissolves freely in cryolite, as was stated in an opinion rendered in January, 1893, by Judge William Howard Taft in the first of a series of lawsuits between the Hall and Cowles interests.[44] Hall also testified in a later case, "The property which cryolite possesses of dissolving alumina freely was not known or made use of prior to the discovery and development of our process." [45] In that same trial, however, an expert witness, Henry Morton, president of Stevens Institute of Technology, testified that Deville in 1859 noted that alumina dissolves in cryolite.[46] As evidence that this fact was widely known before Hall and Héroult, Morton also quoted from Wurtz's *Dictionary of Chemistry*, published in 1868, and from Payen's *Manual of Industrial Chemistry*, published in 1878. He stated that a great number of similar references might be cited and that there was nothing in the wording of these to sustain the contention of witnesses for the defense that prior to Hall it was only known that cryolite would dissolve alumina to a very limited extent, but not that alumina could thus be dissolved freely.

Another witness, O. M. Thowless, an electroplating expert, testified that prior to 1880 he conducted experiments involving the dissolving of alumina in molten cryolite, that he had always known that cryolite would dissolve alumina, and that he supposed that everybody else connected with metallurgical work knew the same.[47] He stated that in attempts to plate surfaces with aluminum in 1875 and 1878 he had found that molten cryolite would dissolve large quantities of alumina.

The results of Hall's experiments with copper anodes, external heating, and baths containing ingredients other than cryolite had been so unsatisfactory during the nine months following July, 1887, that the Cowles brothers informed him in April, 1888, of their final decision not to exercise the option to acquire his patent application. Their business manager, Romaine C. Cole, apparently saw more promise in Hall's process than did his employers. At any rate, in the summer of 1888 he quit the Cowles Company, having persuaded Alfred E. Hunt (1855-1899), a graduate of Massachusetts Institute of Technology and head of the Pittsburgh Testing Laboratory, to raise $20,000 among a few friends for the purpose of developing Hall's ideas. As a result, they incorporated the Pittsburgh Reduction Com-

pany on September 18, 1888.[48] Hall stayed on at the Lockport plant until the latter part of July and in the fall joined
the newly-organized Pittsburgh Reduction Company as its
inventor.

At that time Hall was still employing a commercially unworkable process for producing aluminum. His plant, placed
in operation for the first time on the day before Thanksgiv-
ing, 1888, was designed to use external heat in the form of
gas flames around the crucibles, which were cast-iron open
boxes with the internal surfaces evenly lined with thin layers
of carbon designed for easy transfer from the external heat
source. Thick carbon linings intended to retain the internal
heat would have been indicated where it was contemplated
that internal electric heat would be employed to fuse the
bath.[49] A series of vertical carbon anodes extended down-
ward into each container. It will be recalled that carbon
anodes had always been employed in the Cowles electric furnace and that Hall had been advocating copper anodes. It
was only on September 4, 1888, after he had left the Cowles
plant in Lockport, and when he was beginning work with
the Pittsburgh Reduction Company, that he filed an amend-
ment to his patent application, for the first time dropping the
claims for copper anodes and substituting those involving
carbonaceous anodes.[50]

In view of Hall's failure with external heating while at
Lockport, the most plausible explanation of why he should
have tried it again at Pittsburgh was that he feared the legal
consequences of patent infringement which the Cowles
brothers, and also his promoter, Cole, had intimated to him
would result if he attempted unauthorized use of the internal-heating feature which the Cowles brothers had patented,
and which he had observed in operation while in their employ. At any rate, faced with the failure of his own process,

Hall adopted the Cowles idea through employment of their electric furnace to fuse the bath about two months after the Pittsburgh Reduction Company started operations in the fall of 1888.[51]

Hall apparently at that time still took a dim view of the simple alumina-cryolite solution, as indicated, in fact, by the wording of his patent. A full year after having left the Cowles brothers to join the Pittsburgh Reduction Company, Hall still held the same low opinion of this solution. In a letter dated August 23, 1889, he wrote to his promoter, Romaine C. Cole, "Simple cryolite plus alumina quickly spoils and is no good." [52] He went on to express doubt as to the efficacy of Minet's process which employed a bath for alumina consisting of 30 to 40 per cent cryolite plus 60 to 70 per cent salt. In this letter Hall described as part of his own process what he apparently then regarded as the key to success, namely, the addition of calcium fluoride, or some other earth alkali such as barium or strontium fluoride, plus a large amount of common salt, for the purpose of preserving the cryolite. Even as late as 1892 it appeared that Hall was still favoring the employment of baths other than simple cryolite. An article in *Cassier's Magazine* at that time reported:

Hall changed the proportion of aluminum fluoride to sodium fluoride existing in cryolite by adding a certain quantity of the former, prepared by treating alumina with hydrofluoric acid. He further added a quantity of calcium fluoride (ground fluorspar) to increase the fluidity of the bath. Whether or not this mixture is an improvement has not as yet had final proof, but, so far, it has appeared that the Cowles Electric Smelting and Aluminum Company at Lockport, N.Y., in their experience with the fluoride process, have had less trouble in working with the simple cryolite bath than the Pittsburgh Reduction Company have had with the Hall mixture. . . . The Cowles Company, in practicing

84

the fluoride process, do not use the Hall mixture, and their answer to the charge of infringement is, in brief, that the Hall patents do not cover the use of cryolite pure and simple.[53]

It must be admitted that the answer to the charge of infringement here attributed to the Cowles Company is not well-founded. It is true that Hall in his U.S. Patent No. 400,766 indicated a preference for baths including other ingredients in addition to cryolite but, nevertheless, his claims were so worded as to cover all fluorides of aluminum and sodium, of which cryolite is one.

When the Cowles brothers first undertook to make aluminum by the modern process at Lockport they added alumina to a bath consisting of sodium and cryolite. They soon discovered, however, that the current rapidly eliminated the sodium from the bath, and that the "carbonate of soda" mentioned in Boguski's patent was, therefore, valueless as a part of the mixture. After learning this they ceased to add it to the bath, thereafter dissolving alumina in plain cryolite with excellent results.[54]

The simple cryolite bath was adopted commercially by the Cowles Company near the end of 1890, which was some time after Hall had begun to use their electric furnace. During 1890 the price of aluminum was cut to $1 per pound and in August, 1891, the Cowles Company reduced the price to 50 cents per pound. Seven years before that, in 1884, the price of aluminum had been $15 per pound.

Rivalry between the two pioneer aluminum producing companies was bitter. In the first round of the patent litigation between them the Pittsburgh Reduction Company succeeded in convincing Circuit Judge William Howard Taft that, "The evidence leaves no doubt that the defendant company (the Cowles Company) began their manufacture of pure aluminum in January, 1891, with the aid of one Hobbs, who had been foreman of the complainant company (Pittsburgh Reduction Company), and engaged for it in superintending the manufacture of aluminum by the Hall process." [55] It seems that Judge Taft was unaware of the fact, brought out in a subsequent trial, that John Hobbs for more than two years had been foreman of the Cowles furnace room when in January, 1889, he was hired away from there by the Pittsburgh Reduction Company, presumably in order that he might preside over installation of the Cowles internal electric-heating process in the plant of the Pittsburgh Reduction Company.[56] In taking Hobbs back again in 1891, therefore, the Cowles Company was simply evening the score with its competitor.

The generally-accepted statement that Hall, in his woodshed experiment of February 23, 1886, discovered the modern process for producing aluminum is, to say the least, an over-simplification. During the period from 1886 to 1889, Hall, Héroult, and the Cowles brothers had all been fumbling on the threshold of the sensational discovery. In 1886 Héroult and Hall had experimented with the electrolysis of alumina dissolved in cryolite, but without developing a satisfactory method for fusing the cryolite. In the spring of 1887 the Cowles brothers had actually been the first to employ the modern process experimentally in its entirety, that is, electrolyzing alumina dissolved in cryolite which had been fused by internal electric heat. Their early experiments not being satisfactory, due to impurities in the alumina, they were persuaded by Hall to abandon this line and for a year finance his fruitless experiments with copper anodes, external heat, and baths composed of potassium-aluminum-fluoride or other unsatisfactory ingredients. When Hall finally got on the right track through adoption of the Cowles electric furnace in January, 1889, Héroult at Neuhausen, Switzerland, about that same time abandoned the production of alloys and began the manufacture of aluminum by the modern process.

In 1889 Andrew W. Mellon (1855-1937) first appeared on the aluminum scene. His interest became sufficiently aroused in the new light metal so that he and his brother, Richard B. Mellon (1858-1933), decided to participate in a reorganization of the Pittsburgh Reduction Company as a $1,000,000 corporation, and to make a $250,000 credit available at their Pittsburgh bank, T. Mellon and Sons, in return for being given an influential position in the company. The Mellons' influence was exercised in the beginning through the extension of bank credit, rather than through stock ownership.

Mellon men were always well-treated financially and Hall was no exception. In the 1889 reorganization of the Pittsburgh Reduction Company the capitalization was increased to 10,000 shares of $100 par value, of which Hall was given 3,525 shares and Cole 1,175 shares. Hall is reported to have retained all of his original holdings except 400 shares transferred to members of his family and 60 which he sold to Andrew W. Mellon. He bought 35 of Cole's shares.[57] Contrary to the fate of the traditional poor inventor, Hall, at his death in 1914, is thought to have been worth about $30,000,000.[58] There can be little doubt that this was the greatest financial reward ever received for a single invention by anyone in the world. Cole found after a few years that he was unable to work with Hall and by January, 1893, had sold all of his stock in the Company.[59] He died about 1899 [60] when under 40 years of age. Cole's original holdings, if retained intact through December 31, 1956, would have been worth over $300,000,000 and Hall's over $900,000,000.[61]

NOTES

[1] Edwards, Frary, and Jeffries, *op. cit.*, I, 12, 17.

[2] French Patent No. 175,711, issued April 23, 1886.

[3] Charles C. Carr, *Alcoa, An American Enterprise* (New York: Rinehart & Co., 1952), p. 14.

[4] French Patent No. 175,711 issued on April 23, 1886. For text of this patent see Appendix B.

[5] E.S. & A. Co. *vs.* P.R. Co., 1901 case, Complainant's Proofs, p. 485.

[6] E.S. & A. Co. *vs.* P.R. Co., 1901 case, Complainant's Proofs, pp. 107, 126-27.

[7] British Patent No. 1214, issued on May 13, 1861, to Thomas Bell as agent for Louis Le Chatelier of Paris. For text of this patent see Appendix B.

[8] French Patent No. 155,333, issued on May 10, 1883, to Julien Edward Varin of Epinal (Vosges), France. For text of this patent see Appendix B.

[9] British Patent No. 551, issued January 3, 1884, to Lorentz Albert Groth as agent for Richard Grätzel of Hanover, Germany.

[10] Issued April 2, 1889, as U.S. Patent No. 400,664. For text of this patent see Appendix B.

[11] E.S. & A. Co. *vs.* P.R. Co., 1901 case, Complainant's Proofs, p. 479.

[12] *Ibid.*, p. 161.

[13] *Ibid.*, pp. 162 and 165.

[14] *Ibid.*, p. 432.

[15] *Ibid.*, p. 433.

[16] *Ibid.*, pp. 454-55.

[17] *Ibid.*, pp. 159-60.

[18] *Ibid.*, p. 161.

[19] *Ibid.*, pp. 85-87.

[20] U.S. Patent No. 319,795.

[21] E.S. & A. Co. *vs.* P.R. Co., 1901 case, Defendant's Proofs, p. 79.

[22] Paper read by Alfred H. Cowles at American Electrochemical Society meeting in April, 1927, Philadelphia.

[23] E.S. & A. Co. *vs.* P.R. Co., 1901 case, Defendant's Proofs, p. 80.

[24] *Ibid.*, p. 80.

[25] *Ibid.*, Complainant's Proofs, pp. 552-56.

[26] *Ibid.*, pp. 146-47.

[27] Edwards, Frary & Jeffries, *op. cit.*, I, 26-27. The word "Alcoa" has come into general use as an abbreviation of "Aluminum Company of America."

[28] *Ibid.*, pp. 23-24.

[29] Richards, *op. cit.*, pp. 46-47.

CHARLES MARTIN HALL

[30] Seabury Mastick, "Chemical Patents," *Journal of Industrial and Engineering Chemistry*, October, 1915, p. 881.
[31] U.S. Patent No. 400,766. For text of this patent see Appendix B.
[32] U.S. Patent No. 400,664. For text of this patent see Appendix B.
[33] Anderson, *op. cit.*, pp. 41-42.
[34] Richards, *op. cit.*, p. 46.
[35] E.S. & A. Co. *vs.* P.R. Co., 1901 case, Complainant's Proofs, pp. 480-81.
[36] *Ibid.*, pp. 103-6.
[37] *Ibid.*, p. 553.
[38] *Ibid.*, pp. 103-6, 150.
[39] This affidavit by Cole, in the form of a typewritten draft signed by him, two witnesses, and a notary public, is dated October 10, 1888, but references to it in subsequent court testimony, and evidence in the statement itself, indicate that it probably was made in 1898 and that the date 1888 appears therefore as the result of a typographical error.
[40] Edwards, Frary, and Jeffries, *op. cit.*, I, 22.
[41] Edwards, Frary, and Jeffries, *op. cit.*, pp. 21-22; Carr, *op. cit.*, p. 14; Junius Edwards, *The Immortal Woodshed* (New York: Dodd, Mead & Co., 1955), p. 75; Junius Edwards, *A Captain in Industry* (New York, privately printed, 1957), p. 33.
[42] Terms of the two option agreements, executed as of July 26 and October 22, 1887, are given in the report of E.S. & A. Co. *vs.* P.R. Co., 1901 case, Complainant's Exhibits, pp. 73-75.
[43] E.S. & A. Co. *vs.* P.R. Co., 1901 case, Complainant's Proofs, p. 95.
[44] Pittsburgh Reduction Co. *vs.* Cowles Electric Smelting & Aluminum Co., C.C.N.D., Ohio, 1893, 55 Fed. 301 at 304-5.
[45] E.S. & A. Co. *vs.* P.R. Co., 1901 case, Complainant's Proofs, p. 95.
[46] *Ibid.*, pp. 723-28.
[47] *Ibid.*, pp. 1090-95.
[48] Edwards, Frary, and Jeffries, *op. cit.*, I, 23.
[49] Edwards, *A Captain in Industry*, *op. cit.*, p. 46.
[50] Mastick, *op. cit.*, p. 986.
[51] E.S. & A. Co. *vs.* P.R. Co., 1901 case, Defendant's Proofs, pp. 183 and 193-94.
[52] *Ibid.*, Complainant's Exhibits, Hall-Cole letter No. 9, pp. 13-14.
[53] E. P. Allen, "The Production of Aluminum," *Cassier's Magazine*, February, 1892, pp. 297, 303-4.
[54] E.S. & A. Co. *vs.* P.R. Co., 1901 case, Complainant's Proofs, p. 256.
[55] Pittsburgh Reduction Co. *vs.* Cowles Electric Smelting and Aluminum Co., C.C.N.D., Ohio, 1893, 55 Fed., p. 301. Quotation from Judge Taft's decree.
[56] E.S. & A. Co. *vs.* P.R. Co., 1901 case, Complainant's Proofs, p. 137.

[57] Edwards, *A Captain in Industry, op. cit.,* p. 50; Edwards, *The Immortal Woodshed, op. cit.,* pp. 113, 166, 176-77.

[58] Carr, *op. cit.,* p. 19.

[59] Edwards, *The Immortal Woodshed, op. cit.,* p. 113.

[60] E.S. & A. Co. *vs.* P.R. Co., 1901 case, Complainant's Proofs, pp. 520-21.

[61] These figures have been adjusted to reflect the 1925 merger in which the Aluminum Company of America (Alcoa) acquired Canadian Manufacturing and Development Company which controlled Saguenay River water power. Wallace, *op. cit.,* p. 136. For the period from 1928 to 1956 all adjustments for mergers, stock dividends, rights, etc., are in accordance with the historical record of Alcoa and Aluminium Limited common stocks published by Investographs, Incorporated, of Rochester, New York.

Chapter VII

Paul Louis Toussaint Héroult

During the period under consideration important develments were also occurring abroad where the principal figure was Héroult. He was born in 1863 at Thury-Harcourt in the Calvados district of France. At the age of 15 he first became interested in aluminum through reading the book *de l'Aluminium* by his fellow-countryman Deville. Later he studied natural science, physics, chemistry, and mechanics at Saint-Barbe College which Deville had also attended.

Héroult's father had at one time been employed in a plant at Salindres in southern France where aluminum was manufactured by the Deville chemical process.[1] This undoubtedly had something to do with the younger Héroult's early interest in the electrolysis of various compounds of aluminum. He undertook a series of experiments in this field when at the death of his father in 1885 he inherited a small tannery at Gentilly equipped with a steam engine to which he added a Gramme dynamo. As a result of considerable work along these lines he conceived the idea of electrolyzing alumina dissolved in molten cryolite for which his French patent application was filed in April, 1886, two and one-half months before Hall filed his United States patent application covering the same idea.[2] Speaking at the Metallurgical Congress in Paris during the World's Fair in 1900, Héroult described his experiments, commenced in 1885, which led to his accidental discovery of this process. He told of his futile attempts to obtain aluminum by electrolysis of aque‧ous solutions, and also of experiments with cryolite which at first were unsuccessful. In this latter connection he said:

Having tried to lower the temperature of the electrolyte (cryolite) by mixing the double chloride of sodium and aluminum with it, I was surprised to find that the carbon anode showed obvious signs of attack. I concluded that I was dealing with an oxide whose reduction was effected at the expense of the anode. After investigation, I found that what I had bought for double chloride was, in reality, alumina resulting from the decomposition of the chloride by moisture. From this it was but a step to discover the present process used for the manufacture of aluminum.

According to Héroult's account, his next move was to consult A. R. Pechiney,[3] head of the plant at Salindres in southern France where his father had been employed in the production of aluminum by the Deville chemical process which its inventor 30 years before had installed there.[4] Pechiney advised Héroult against attempting to manufacture pure aluminum, pointing out that there was then more demand for aluminum alloys, especially aluminum bronze.[5] Héroult thereupon developed a process for the manufacture of aluminum bronze on which he took out a French patent dated April 15, 1887.

The drawing and specification of his April 23, 1886, patent indicated the use of external heat to fuse the cryolite bath in which the alumina was to be dissolved, and this also was true of the application for his British patent, filed on May 21, 1887. However, the complete revised specification for this British patent, dated March 21, 1888, mentioned the use of internal electric heat to fuse the bath, and one observer reported on June 21, 1887, that Héroult was then producing aluminum bronze, using internal electric heat to fuse the ore.[6] This placed him 19 months prior to Hall in the use of an internally-heated furnace but the Cowles brothers, of course, had already begun to employ their electric furnace commercially in 1885 to produce aluminum bronze and other alloys and had at that time given considerable publicity to the idea. Alfred H. Cowles later testified that Héroult's process for the production of aluminum bronze was at first a commercial failure, but that it was made successful through knowledge gained of the Cowles process and the resulting adoption of internal electric heat, thicker walls for the pots, and appropriate regulation of the current.[7]

So far as the production of aluminum alloys was concerned, the Cowles brothers for the time being dominated the field in Great Britain. In 1887 they completed at Milton, Stoke-on-Trent, Staffordshire, England, a plant for the Cowles Syndicate Company which they had organized.[8] In that year they installed there a 500 horsepower motor generator, the largest yet built in any country.[9] It was inspected by many experts as a notable triumph in electrical engineering.[10] The Cowles works at Milton, according to the *History of the British Aluminium Company,* had the distinction of being the first electrometallurgical plant in Europe.[11]

Some time in 1887 a group of Berlin investors with important financial backing became interested in undertaking the production of aluminum bronze in Germany. A clash thereupon developed between the Cowles and Héroult interests in that country as a result of which the German courts in 1888 upheld the Cowles patent rights there against Héroult on the issue of internal electric smelting of the ore.[12] The Berlin group then, on July 6, 1888, offered $404,765 for the Cowles patent rights covering all of Europe except Great Britain, France, and Belgium.[13] While this offer was being negotiated, with a difference of only $20,000 between the price the Cowles Company was asking and the German offer, Lowrey, the Western Union patent lawyer who eight years before had organized the Edison Company, suggested to these Germans that they participate in a development at Neuhausen, Switzerland, employing Héroult's process. He pointed out that, because in Switzerland there were as yet no patent laws in effect, they could thus avoid having to buy the Cowles patent rights.[14] As a result of this the German offer to the Cowles Company was withdrawn in October, 1888, and instead the Germans purchased for 40,000 pounds (about $175,000) the Héroult plant at the Rhine Falls in Switzerland as well as certain of his European patent rights.[15]

This German group was reported to have been headed by "Rathenau who later became director of German industries during World War I." [16] Walther Rathenau (1867-1922), the famous German industrialist and statesman, was head of the Board of War Ministry which controlled the administration of German war materials in the first World War. In 1888, however, he was only 21 years old and a student in German universities.[17] Presumably this German syndicate was headed, not by Walther Rathenau, but by his father, Emil Rathenau, who also was an important industrialist, and founder of Allgemeine Elektrizitats-Gesellschaft which participated with certain Swiss interests in founding the Aluminium Industrie Aktiengesellschaft at the Rhine Falls, Neuhausen, Switzerland, for the purpose of producing aluminum and aluminum bronze by Héroult's process. Walther Rathenau, upon completion of his studies at Munich in 1890, took a position as a civil engineer with this Neuhausen firm. Héroult's agent, Lowrey, was the same patent attorney who in 1897 lost a legal contest with the Cowles Company over ownership of the Bradley patents.[18]

Additional light was thrown on the early Swiss activities in testimony by Albert Stetson, a New York electrical engineer and patent expert who said that in the beginning there was more aluminum put onto the market by manufacturers under the Héroult process than could possibly be absorbed.[19] He reported that the people at Neuhausen, after spending more than a million dollars and employing the best commercial travelers to be found in Europe, were very much disheartened when their travelers returned without having sold metal enough to pay the cost of their samples. Stetson also testified that the establishment at Neuhausen for several years manufactured more aluminum than all other producers in the world combined.

From 1887 to 1890 the Cowles Syndicate Company dominated the aluminum bronze field in England and Héroult carried on in Switzerland. In 1890 a subsidiary of the Pittsburgh Reduction Company established a plant at Patricroft in Lancashire [20] and some time near the end of that year it and the Cowles Syndicate Company began to employ commercially in England the modern alumina-cryolite process for the production of aluminum. When manufacture of the pure metal supplanted that of the alloy the situation developed in such a way that the owner of Hall's patent gained ascendancy in the United States whereas Héroult prevailed in various European countries including Switzerland, France, and England. The Hall and Cowles companies were ultimately forced out of business in England by the British Aluminium Company, Limited, organized on May 7, 1894, which had acquired the British patents of Héroult and Karl Joseph Bayer, a German who in 1888 had originated a process for the production of alumina from bauxite ore. These patents gave the British Aluminium Company a monopoly of its field in England and thereafter it became the dominant aluminum company in the British Empire. It took over the Cowles Syndicate Company plant at Milton which to this day it operates as a rolling mill.

Héroult at different stages of his career participated in at least two enterprises in the United States. He had an excellent command of the English language, having stayed with his grandfather in England during the war of 1870. He helped to organize the United States Aluminum Metal Company which in July, 1889, established under his personal direction at Bridgeport, Connecticut, and later at Boonton, New Jersey, plants for the production of aluminum and aluminum bronze, employing Héroult's process.[21] According to Alfred H. Cowles, the Cowles Company filed suit against this company, alleging infringement of Cowles patents.[22] The United States Aluminum Metal Company discontinued operations before its program had progressed beyond the experimental stage. Héroult again participated in a United States venture when in August, 1912, he undertook to supervise construction of a power plant and reduction works for the Southern Aluminium Company in North Carolina.[23] From about 1900 until his death in 1914 he devoted considerable time to the iron and steel industry. The Héroult steel furnace was the most popular one of his day in England and he is, in fact, generally credited with having been the pioneer in applying electrometallurgy in that field.

NOTES

[1] E.S. & A. Co. *vs.* P.R. Co., 1901 case, Complainant's Proofs, p. 122.

[2] A substantial part of the information on Héroult in this and the following paragraphs is from Edwards, Frary, and Jeffries, *op. cit.*, I, 35-37.

[3] Wallace, *op. cit.*, p. 512.

[4] Edwards, Frary, and Jeffries, *op. cit.*, I, 39.

[5] Wallace, *op. cit.*, p. 512.

[6] E.S. & A. Co. *vs.* P.R. Co., 1901 case, Complainant's Exhibits, Report of M. Brivet of Paris, pp. 98-100.

[7] *Ibid.,* Complainant's Proofs, pp. 155-56.

[8] U.S. Patent Office hearing, Cowles *vs.* Rody, October 23, 1916, p. 2. See also Hartford, *op. cit.,* p. 9. See also J. N. Pring, *The Electric Furnace* (London: Longmans, Green & Co., 1921), preface, p. vii.

[9] Hartford, *op. cit.,* p. 9. See also Pring, *op. cit.,* preface, p. vii.

[10] John B. C. Kershaw, *Electrometallurgy* (New York: D. Van Nostrand Co., 1908), p. 15.

[11] *History of British Aluminium Co.* (London: Norfolk House, 1955), p. 13.

[12] Lowrey *vs.* Cowles Electric Smelting & Aluminum Co., C.C.A. 6th Circuit, Ohio, 1897, Defendant's Proofs, pp. 260-61 (decision reported 79 Fed. 331). See also E.S. & A. Co. *vs.* P.R. Co., 1901 case, Complainant's Proofs, pp. 281-84.

[13] E.S. & A. Co. *vs.* P.R. Co., 1901 case, Complainant's Proofs, pp. 152-55. This episode was also described by Alfred H. Cowles in a paper read at the meeting of the American Electrochemical Society in Philadelphia in April, 1927, at which he exhibited the cablegram in which the offer was made.

[14] The first patent law of Switzerland was enacted on June 29, 1888, and became effective on November 15 of that year. See *Patent Laws of the World* (London: Chartered Institute of Patent Agents, 1899 edition), pp. 349-59.

[15] Reported in letter of October 26, 1888, to the Cowles Company from Ben M. Plumb, London agent for the Cowles interests.

[16] Hartford, *op. cit.,* p. 9. See also U.S. Patent Office hearing, Fauré *vs.* Cowles & Cowles *vs.* Bradley & Crocker, December 3, 1888, p. 69.

[17] *Encyclopaedia Britannica,* 1953 ed., XVIII, 990-91.

[18] See pp. 53-54.

[19] E.S. & A. Co. *vs.* P.R. Co., 1901 case, Complainant's Proofs, p. 1061.

[20] Edwards, Frary, and Jeffries, *op. cit.,* I, 44.

[21] Richards, *op. cit.,* p. 396.

[22] Lowrey *vs.* Cowles Electric Smelting and Aluminum Co., C.C.A. 6th Circuit, Ohio, 1897, Defendant's Proofs, pp. 258-59 (decision reported 79 Fed. 331).

[23] Wallace, *op. cit.,* p. 115.

Chapter VIII

Patent Litigation

By 1891 an impasse was reached in the United States between the Cowles and Hall interests. Since for economical production the Pittsburgh Reduction Company needed the electric furnace of the Cowles Company, and the Cowles Company needed the Pittsburgh Reduction Company's idea of electrolyzing alumina dissolved in molten cryolite, neither one could manufacture aluminum by the modern low-cost process without infringing a patent owned by the other. An attempt was made, with Romaine C. Cole as intermediary, to merge the two companies.[1] When this failed, with the Pittsburgh people accusing Cole of being too friendly towards their rival, the Cowles Company on January 17, 1891, brought suit against the Pittsburgh Reduction Company for infringement of the Cowles patent and the Pittsburgh Reduction Company on February 11, 1891, filed a bill of complaint against the Cowles Company, alleging infringement of the Hall patent. In modern times it would be very unusual for business fortunes of the kind at stake in this situation to be left in such uncertain hands as those of the courts. The normal solution would be the exchange of patent rights through cross-license arrangements. Here, however, the matter was left to the courts and, as it turned out, a death blow was dealt to the Cowles Company despite the fact that it won the final round of the litigation.

The first decision in the long series of lawsuits was handed down January 20, 1893, by Judge William Howard Taft, then 35 years of age, sitting in one of his first cases as judge in the Federal Circuit Court for the Northern District of Ohio.[2] The Taft decision enjoined further production of aluminum by the Cowles Company and kept its plant closed for 10 years. Promptly after the decision the price of aluminum, which had fallen to 50 cents per pound through competition between the two companies, was increased sharply as buyers found that they had either to pay the Pittsburgh Reduction Company's price or go without aluminum.

The Taft decision, which gave Hall entire credit for the increase in production of aluminum, left unanswered a number of legal and factual questions, particularly in the light of evidence on hand today which may not have been available at the time of that trial. At any rate Judge Wing on April 4, 1903, sitting in the same court, virtually annulled the appraisal of Hall's contribution made by Taft in his decision (though not the injurious commercial effect of the decision on the Cowles Company) by reopening the case on the ground that additional evidence of importance had become available.[3] One of the defenses urged upon Judge Taft by the Cowles Company was that the process described in the Hall patent was inoperable. The United States Constitution and statutes under it provide for the grant of patents only for those inventions which are "useful." Accordingly, if what was shown in the Hall patent was not "useful" because not operable, then the patent was invalid. Judge Taft in his written opinion alluded to this defense and dismissed it summarily by reference to the fact that the Pittsburgh Reduction Company was producing large quantities of aluminum at a low price, but this left open the question as to whether it was actually using the Hall patented process for this production.

During the 1893 trial before Judge Taft the defense did not have available the 1889 correspondence in which Hall repudiated as "no good" the cryolite bath, appropriation of which by the Cowles Company constituted his basis for that suit.[4] This correspondence,[5] which did not come to light until 1898,[6] might have raised serious doubts in Judge Taft's mind as to whether commercial success of the Pittsburgh Reduction Company was due solely to ideas embodied in the Hall patent or whether, until the Cowles idea of internal heating was adopted, and its adaptation to the Hall process perfected, Hall was quite right in saying that dissolving alumina in cryolite was "no good." On the basis of Hall's own estimate Taft could hardly have upheld the Hall patent.

The Taft decision, in addition to enjoining the Cowles Company, provided for an accounting for damages before a master, and in this accounting the question arose as to how much of the success of the Cowles Company was due to the Hall invention and how much to others, including the electric-furnace invention of the Cowles brothers themselves. It was after the master had taken testimony on these points that Judge Wing was petitioned to reopen the case, and it was on the basis of some of the testimony before the master that the case was opened for new evidence. In Judge Wing's opinion he said:

In view of Judge Taft's opinion, it is most important to a correct decision of this cause that full information should be had upon the question as to whether *commercial success* resulted from the practice of the process described in the complainant's patent, or some important modification of, or addition to, such process. Judge Taft was much influenced in his decision by the fact, as it then appeared to him from the proofs, that Hall, by his process, had reduced the cost of production of aluminum in a most marked degree. Important testimony is proposed to be offered on the question as to whether or not internal heating sufficient to fuse is necessarily incident to the use of the electric current in electrolysis. There are other important questions raised by a consideration of the proposed new testimony, the solution of which seems essential to a correct final decree. I am fully appreciative of the weight and importance which should be given to the decision of so able a jurist as Judge Taft, and am of the opinion that, had he the cause before him as now presented upon this petition, unless restrained by the consideration of some imperative rule of practice in equity, he would give the defendant the opportunity of supplementing its proof in the manner prayed for.[7] [Italics added.]

This case never came to trial again because the Cowles Company in 1903 won the appeal in the trial of the Bradley patent and thereupon negotiated a settlement with the Pittsburgh Reduction Company which also covered the points at issue in the 1893 trial of the Hall patent before Judge Taft. The issue of the Bradley patent in 1892 came as a great surprise to the Pittsburgh Reduction Company as indicated by the following letter from Hall to Cole, written on December 9, 1891:

Dear Cole: I write to you on what may be a very important matter in our case with the Cowles Company. Will you please find out at once and let me know by telegram to Pittsburgh on Monday or Sunday if you find anything, who Charles S. Bradley, the patentee in the Bradley & Crocker patent, is and where he can be got at now. His address on the patent is Yonkers, N.Y. and I understand he is not there at present. . . . Bradley has recently had a patent issued on fusing and electrolyzing by the electric current. He has broad claims in the office which may or may not be rejected, which would cover our commercial method of working and his applications date back to 1883. His patent issued counts for nothing and it is what may be back of them that interests us. Hunt telegraphed on Christy's advice, to find him and see him while here to prevent the Cowles Co. from buying him up. Please find out what you can at once and let us know and don't let any portion of the enemy know what you are about. What makes it more important is that we know that some of Bradley's claims still in the Office are allowed but we do not know their scope and value positively.

Yours hastily, Chas. M. Hall.[8]

The Hall contingent was not the only group to be startled by the unexpected appearance of the Bradley patent. The Cowles Company itself was confronted with a serious problem in its suit charging the Pittsburgh Reduction Company with infringing the Cowles patent. Due to a peculiarity in the law [9] the Cowles patent probably could have been invalidated on the ground that Bradley's patent held priority over theirs even though the Cowles brothers had been able to prove that they had conceived their idea prior to Bradley's filing date and that they had exercised proper diligence in reducing it to practice. It therefore was necessary for the Cowles Company, first to establish its ownership of the Bradley patent, and then to substitute it as the basis for litigation with the Pittsburgh Reduction Company. Withdrawal of the Cowles suit, filed in 1891, charging infringement of their patent, was thus forced on the Cowles interests through realization that all the Pittsburgh people probably had to do in order to win that case was to cite the important Bradley patent against the Cowles patent. This situation was not clarified until the Court of Appeals finally in 1897 decided that the Cowles Company held title to the Bradley patent.

After its ownership of the Bradley patent had been established by the Court of Appeals in 1897 the Cowles Company, by then reorganized as the Electric Smelting and Aluminum Company, sued the Pittsburgh Reduction Company for infringement of the Bradley patent. In the case before the New York lower court in 1901, Judge Hazel held that the Bradley patent had not been infringed.[10] The Cowles Company appealed the case and in 1903 the Court of Appeals held that the Bradley patent was valid and that it was infringed by the Hall process as used by the Pittsburgh Reduction Company.[11] In each of these trials the principal issue before the court was the question, thoroughly debated by experts, of the relationship between the current required for electrolysis, on the one hand, and for electrolysis with heating, on the other hand. Under patent law the general rule is that a mere change of degree is not invention, that is, if upon doubling the electric current the only result were to double the amount of aluminum produced, this would not be regarded as invention. If, however, the result is "surprising," that is, if it is something more than merely quantitatively better, then the change is held to be invention. In the appeal of the suit under the Bradley patent the evidence indicated that a certain increase in the scale of operation called for a corresponding increase in the amount of electric current needed for electrolysis. This resulted in the current used for electrolysis generating sufficient heat to fuse the bath, whereas on a smaller scale the amount of current suitable for electrolysis was insufficient to fuse the bath. The court found that this increase in electric current and scale of operation, while keeping the voltage within limits suitable for electrolysis, altered the process from one which had little or no practical utility to one which was of great practical value, that it therefore constituted invention, and that in employing it the Pittsburgh Reduction Company was infringing the Bradley patent.

In the final suit [12] in which the Cowles Company asserted the Bradley patent [13] against the Pittsburgh Reduction Company, Judges Wallace, Lacombe, and Coxe, in the New York Court of Appeals on October 29, 1903, held the Pittsburgh Reduction Company to be liable for court costs and damages which, according to Professor Wallace, totaled almost $3,000,000.[14] While we have not been able to find any court record as to the amount, this figure does not seem unreasonable in view of the extent and duration of the infringement. As it turned out, the Cowles Company back in 1885 had acquired quite a bargain in purchasing for $5000 title to an application for the Bradley patent which it used later as the basis for this infringement suit. It must be remembered, however, that the Cowles Company in 1888 decided not to exercise an option whereby it might have secured title to Hall's important patent in return for one-eighth of the Cowles Company's outstanding stock, at that time worth possibly $30,000.[15] Hall shortly thereafter received in payment for his patent rights a 35.25 per cent interest in the Pittsburgh Reduction Company and this holding constituted the principal part of his estate, said to have amounted to about $30,000,000 at his death 25 years later.[16] On an overall basis, therefore, the Cowles Company's record of success at the bargain counter appears to have been something less than 100 per cent.

The New York Court of Appeals, in its 1903 opinion written by Judge Coxe, stated that the Hall process in which cryolite was used as a bath for alumina, while an improvement upon, was also an infringement of the plaintiff's process when practiced with internal heat for fusing the ore, and that a patent process cannot be appropriated because the infringer practices it with a new, enlarged, and improved apparatus. In commenting on the history of aluminum Judge Coxe said:

Not only did the electricians of the earlier art fail to produce aluminum by electricity alone, but the wrecks which strew the pathway which Davy pointed out nearly a century ago, offer mute but impressive proof of the genius of the man who first surmounted its many obstacles and reached the destination in safety. Indeed, after numerous abortive attempts and repeated failures, the electrical world seemed to have settled down into the belief that aluminum could not be produced by the sole agency of electricity. Accordingly, the effort of inventors was directed to the perfection of processes in which external heat was employed to melt the ore and keep it in a fused state. . . . Patent after patent was introduced claiming new methods of separating aluminum from its ores, but in every instance external fire was used to fuse the bath and maintain it in a fused condition. Many of these inventions were long after the introduction of dynamos. . . . Indeed, so strongly was the inventive trend toward the employment of external heat that even the defendant's inventor, Hall, could not be induced to dispense with its use until 1889. When the defendant's works were started at Pittsburgh, in December, 1888, the pots were built to be externally heated and they were so heated for some time thereafter. In the Hall patent of April 2, 1889, which was applied for July 9, 1886, three years after the Bradley application, externally-heated crucibles are shown in the drawing and described in the specification.

The Mellon interests evidently did not consider their chances of victory sufficiently good to justify appealing the case to the Supreme Court of the United States. They therefore participated in the negotiation of a settlement whereby the Pittsburgh Reduction Company canceled its claim for $293,908 damages previously decreed by Judge Taft against the Cowles Company and instead agreed to pay the Cowles interests $250,000 plus royalties on all aluminum manufactured from October 31, 1903, until expiration of the Bradley patent in 1909.[17] These royalties were at the rate of one and one-half cents per pound on the first 8,000,000 pounds manufactured in any given year, and one cent per pound on any excess over that amount. In addition to very substantial court costs, total payments by the defendants to the Cowles Company amounted to about $1,200,000. The Pittsburgh Reduction Company, however, received exclusive rights to manufacture aluminum under the Bradley patent and the Cowles foothold was thus lost in the rapidly-growing aluminum industry while the Mellon group's control became further entrenched.

It may seem surprising that the Cowles interests would have made such a concession at a time when they had just won an important court action against their rival and when they, temporarily at least through patent control, dominated the field of electric smelting. Actually, their position was not nearly so strong as it might on the surface appear to have been. Electric smelting was still in its infancy and their royalties, received mainly from manufacturers of calcium carbide and phosphorus, were quite small when contrasted with the 1903 earnings of the Pittsburgh Reduction Company, now estimated to have been in excess of $1,300,000. Furthermore, Hall's patent still had four years to run so that, unless the Taft decision was reversed, the Cowles Company could not manufacture aluminum by the modern process before 1906 although it had the power to close down the Pittsburgh Reduction Company's plant till 1909, provided in the meantime it did not lose the appeal to the Supreme Court. Actually by 1903 the financial position of the Cowles family had deteriorated to a point where there was grave doubt as to whether it could continue much longer the by then unequal battle with the powerful Mellon group. The death of Edwin Cowles in 1890 had deprived the *Cleveland Leader* and *Cleveland Evening News* of their editor and publisher. His oldest son, Eugene, had also died in 1892 and Alfred, who was primarily a scientist and inventor, had been preoccupied for 10 years from 1893 to 1903 with the legal and financial problems of their closed-down aluminum company. Earnings of the *Leader* and *Evening News* had gone into a decline, through lack of management combining adequate ability with journalistic experience, and the family was finally forced to sell the newspapers at a price of $300,000.

After expiration of the Hall patent in 1906 an investment in excess of $5,000,000 might have been required to launch an enterprise on a scale which would enable it to compete with the Pittsburgh Reduction Company which by then was well on the way to establishing itself in control of this country's available sources of bauxite and alumina. In those days it was not easy to persuade bankers to underwrite new ventures in the aluminum industry, where volume of production, costs, and profit margins were jealously guarded trade secrets known only to the Pittsburgh Reduction Company, nor did the Cowles Company have at its command sufficient financial resources to justify continuing to engage its rival in further prolonged legal battles with the possibility of an adverse Supreme Court decision at that end. It was undoubtedly because of considerations such as these that the Cowles Company felt constrained to accept the settlement whereby the Pittsburgh Reduction Company acquired a legal monopoly of the aluminum industry for six years until the Bradley patent expired in 1909.

In view of the fact that the Cowles Company chose in 1897 to assert the Bradley patent in its litigation with the Pittsburgh Reduction Company an interesting question is raised by the Cowles Company's electing to assert the Cowles patent in its successful action against the Carborundum Company. The initial reason for this course is clear in view of the fact that suit against the Carborundum Company was filed before the date in 1897 when Cowles ownership of the Bradley patent became established, but the Pittsburgh Reduction Company litigation was concluded in 1903, ten years before the final decision in the Carborundum Company case. Just why no attempt was made by the Carborundum Company to invalidate the Cowles patent by citing the priority of Bradley's filing date is not entirely clear. Because of the Mellon family's large interest, both in the Carborundum Company and the Aluminum Company of America (Alcoa), it seems certain that the Carborundum Company would have known about the Pittsburgh Reduction Company litigation in which the Cowles Company asserted the Bradley patent in preference to its own, and it would have been natural for the Carborundum Company to attack the Cowles patent on the basis of Bradley's priority if such a course had seemed practicable. Several reasons may be advanced as to why this did not occur. One of these is that all the facts as to priority might not have been known to the defendants, so that they would have been uncertain as to the results of a foray into such a line of defense, but that would not explain why in this case the Cowles Company chose to assert the Cowles rather than the Bradley patent. A more likely explanation seems to be that the Cowles Company was relying on the assumption that the Bradley patent did not concern itself with the making of carborundum, so that Bradley's prior filing date would not invalidate the work of the Cowles brothers in this field.

NOTES

[1] Affidavit of Romaine C. Cole. See footnote 39, p. 89.

[2] Pittsburgh Reduction Co. *vs.* Cowles Electric Smelting & Aluminum Co., C.C.N.D., Ohio, E.D., 1893, 55 Fed. 301.

[3] Pittsburgh Reduction Co. *vs.* Cowles Electric Smelting & Aluminum Co., C.C.N.D., Ohio, E.D., 1903, 121 Fed. 557. Date of decision is not shown in the official report but is established by the following references: A. H. Cowles deposition in U.S. Patent Office hearing, A. H. Cowles *vs.* Franz A. Rody, October 23, 1916, pp. 2-3; also Alfred H. Cowles's April, 1927, reply to paper by Edwards at American Electrochemical Society meeting in Philadelphia, p. 7.

[4] E.S. & A. Co. *vs.* P.R. Co., 1901 case, Complainant's Exhibits, Hall-Cole letter No. 9, p. 1204.

[5] See p. 84.

[6] E.S. & A. Co. *vs.* P.R. Co., 1901 case, Complainant's Proofs, p. 521.

[7] Pittsburgh Reduction Co. *vs.* Cowles Electric Smelting & Aluminum Co., C.C.N.D., Ohio, E.D., 1903, 121 Fed. 557.

[8] E.S. & A. Co. *vs.* P.R. Co., 1901 case, Complainant's Exhibits, Hall-Cole letter No. 20, pp. 51-52.

[9] See pp. 56-59.

[10] C.C.W.D., New York, 1901, 111 Fed. 742.

[11] C.C.A. 2nd, New York, 1903, 125 Fed. 926.

[12] Electric Smelting & Aluminum Co. *vs.* Pittsburgh Reduction Co., C.C.A. 2nd, New York, 1903, 125 Fed. 926.

[13] U.S. Patent No. 468,148, issued February 2, 1892.

[14] Wallace, *op. cit.,* p. 536.

[15] Edwin Cowles testified that he had invested $250,000 in the Cowles inventions. See U.S. Patent Office hearing, Fauré *vs.* Cowles & Cowles *vs.* Bradley & Crocker, December 3, 1888, p. 59.

[16] In 1907 the Pittsburgh Reduction Company's name was changed to Aluminum Company of America (Alcoa). Its earnings in 1914, the year of Hall's death, are estimated by Wallace, *op. cit.,* p. 544, to have been $7,500,000 before interest on funded debt, the amount of which, if any, is not reported. At ten times these earnings the 35 per cent of outstanding Alcoa stock remaining in the possession of Hall and other members of his family would have been worth $26,250,000.

[17] This settlement was in the form of an exclusive license agreement. The text of this agreement appears as Exhibit 265, U.S.D.C.S.D., New York, 1941, 44 Fed. Sup. 97.

Chapter IX

Aluminum Monopoly

The place of Andrew W. and Richard B. Mellon in this account is naturally of interest. Following the grant of $250,000 credit to the Pittsburgh Reduction Company in 1889 the Mellons first acquired stock in this company on January 6, 1890, through purchase of 60 shares from Hall for $6,000 [1] and in 1892 Andrew Mellon served for a while as treasurer of the company.[2] Although the Cowles brothers were not aware of it at the time, this was a very ominous development for them. From 1889 on, their competitor, the Pittsburgh Reduction Company, had on its team a man who has been described as looking like a tired double-entry book-keeper afraid of losing his job, but who in reality was one of the coolest and most resourceful figures in the financial and business history of the United States. It is not generally known what Mellon was worth at his death in 1937, but he, Ford, and Rockefeller during their lifetimes were supposedly the only billionaires.

By May, 1894, the Mellon interest in the Pittsburgh Reduction Company had been increased to 12.35 per cent of the outstanding stock. On January 1, 1907, the name was changed to Aluminum Company of America (Alcoa) and by 1920 the Mellons owned about one-third of the stock.[3] Thereafter the two Mellon brothers and their associate, Arthur Vining Davis, the latter through his own stock and as trustee of Hall's estate, had combined holdings equal to a

majority of the stock of Alcoa.[4] In 1928 this control was extended to include Aluminium Limited, the Canadian affil-
iate established at that time to hold the foreign interests of
Alcoa. The Mellon family interest in Alcoa is said to be today about 28 per cent of the outstanding preferred and
common stock.

One report, commenting in 1933 on Judge Taft's 1893
decision against the Cowles Company, said: "That signature,
'Taft, J.' was worth $100,000,000 to the Mellons." [5] Actu-
ally, by the end of 1956 the Mellon interests in Alcoa and
Aluminium Limited, if their 1933 holdings had been retained intact, would have been worth over $850,000,000. It
is not the intention here to imply that the capital and ad-
ministrative judgment used by the Mellons in the aluminum
industry would have been unprofitable if employed elsewhere, but it is hard to imagine any other situation offering so spectacular an opportunity as a monopoly in production of the most abundant metal on the face of the earth.

When the Cowles plant was closed down by Judge Taft
in 1893 annual production of aluminum in North America
amounted to only about 150 metric tons worth $240,000. It
had increased to 3,300 tons worth $2,400,000, about twenty-
two times the 1893 production, when in 1903 the Cowles
Company won the final victory in its litigation with the
Pittsburgh Reduction Company. The latter had benefited
from all this increase while at the same time the Cowles
Company had suffered heavy financial reverses as a result
of the Taft injunction which prohibited the operation of
its plant for a decade, during which it was also subjected
to continuous and substantial legal expense. It was this 10-
year period, of course, which established the aluminum monopoly in the United States.

The Pittsburgh Reduction Company had by 1903 become
relatively powerful financially as evidenced by the fact that,

although its policy was to retain most of its earnings for development, it nevertheless paid a dividend of $228,000 in 1904. Only since 1926 have annual financial reports been published by Alcoa, but estimates have been made of earnings for the years 1909 to 1926, based on the Company's reports to the Department of Justice, and on other sources.[6] These estimates give Alcoa's earnings before interest, if any, on funded debt [7] as about $3,600,000 in 1909, a year in which its production of primary aluminum was about 12,000 metric tons. In 1904 the Pittsburgh Reduction Company, having enjoyed a monopoly of the industry for 11 years, produced about 3,600 metric tons of primary aluminum, the price per ton being about 66 per cent higher than in 1909. With the same profit margin as in 1909 its 1904 earnings would have been about $1,800,000. It also had the backing of the Mellon banking resources and, in fact, Richard B. Mellon served as its president from 1899 to 1910.[8]

From 1903 to 1909 the Mellon group's monopoly rested on the legal right to an exclusive position conferred by the Bradley patent which the courts had upheld, but the Federal Government in its anti-trust suits claimed that thereafter practices were resorted to which were in restraint of trade. As an example, Alfred H. Cowles testified at a Patent Office hearing in 1916 that since expiration of the Bradley patent in 1909 his company had been unsuccessful in its attempts to get back into production of aluminum because companies producing alumina seemed to be so tied to Alcoa that it was impossible for him to buy alumina from any source on a basis which would permit competition with Alcoa in the production of aluminum.[9] The evidence seems to support his statement. By 1909 there were only four operators mining bauxite in the United States: [10] (1) Aluminum Company of America (Alcoa) which prior to 1900, when known as the Pittsburgh Reduction Company,[11] had acquired substantial bauxite deposits, mainly in Arkansas; (2) General Bauxite Company, purchased in 1905 by the Pittsburgh Reduction Company from the General Chemical Company, a long-term contract having been made with the latter under which it was to be supplied with ores needed for its chemical business on condition that none be used for the production of aluminum; (3) Pennsylvania Salt Manufacturing Company which in 1907 entered into a long-term contract to sell Alcoa 37,500 tons of alumina per year, the seller at the same time agreeing not to enter the business of aluminum reduction or to sell alumina to anyone else for the purpose of making aluminum; (4) Republic Mining and Manufacturing Company which in 1909 was purchased by Alcoa from the Norton Company, manufacturer of abrasives, a long-term contract having been negotiated whereby a 40-acre tract of bauxite land was retained by the Norton Company on condition that the latter agree not to sell or use bauxite for the production of aluminum.

The Government in its 1912 petition for an anti-trust decree claimed that Alcoa had acquired 90 per cent of all known bauxite deposits in the United States and Canada suitable for the production of aluminum. Alcoa denied this but it is likely that after 1909 there were not available in this country many bauxite deposits which could provide an adequate basis for rival ventures in the production of aluminum. Otherwise, there would have been no reason for the restrictive agreements whereby Alcoa prevented raw matrials from being supplied to its potential rivals. Furthermore, no competitors of any importance succeeded in establishing themselves. The restrictive clauses in the contracts whereby the various companies were prevented from selling bauxite or alumina to potential competitors of Alcoa were in 1912 annulled by court decree, but ownership of its bauxite deposits was left with Alcoa.

During the decade from expiration of the Bradley patent in 1909 to the end of the first World War there was only one important attempt made to enter the field of aluminum production in the United States in competition with Alcoa. In August, 1912, Adrian Badin of l'Aluminium Français, and a group of associates in the French aluminum industry, incorporated the Southern Aluminium Company, all stock of which was owned by Europeans. This company acquired the property of an American group which had become involved in financial difficulties while attempting to develop a hydro-electric project on the Yadkin River in central North Carolina. The Southern Aluminium Company employed as its engineer Paul Héroult, the brilliant French inventor who 26 years before had independently of Charles Martin Hall developed the idea of electrolyzing alumina dissolved in molten cryolite, and who had gained extensive experience at aluminum reduction works in Switzerland and France. Under Héroult's direction was launched the construction of a power plant and reduction works with a projected capacity of about 25,000 tons per year. Héroult's participation in this enterprise was terminated by his death in 1914, three months before the outbreak of the first World War. Professor Wallace made the following comments on the Southern Aluminium Company episode:

The new company was assured of an adequate supply of bauxite from the French mines of its owners. Plans to start production in 1913 or 1914 did not materialize when it was found that the partly constructed dam of the predecessor company was poorly located. Just prior to the outbreak of the war it was announced that production would begin in June 1915 at an initial rate of about 5000 tons a year. In October 1914, however, construction operations had to be suspended, owing to the impossibility of further financing in France under war conditions. Up to that time about $5,500,-000 had been spent in acquiring properties and in construction work, and it was estimated that approximately $7,500,-000 was needed to complete the plants. Fruitless endeavors were made to secure the necessary financial assistance in England as well as in France. When application to powerful financial interests in the United States also met with no success, the stockholders, faced with entire loss of the large investment already sunk, negotiated with Aluminum Company of America which . . . purchased the plant on August 15, 1915, for $5,030,000. . . .

The significance of the episode seems to be this. The only thorough-going and serious attempt to enter the field after the expiration of the Bradley patent was made by a group of aluminum producers with long experience, possessing its own bauxite. It was planned to employ an investment of about $10,000,000 in setting up a thoroughly integrated, large-scale concern. . . . When extraordinary conditions (World War I) prevented completion of financing abroad, no American bankers could be induced in 1915 to supply the backing needed to bring operations into being—even with the beckoning force of a rising war demand for aluminum. In the large view, looking through the mists of war uncertainty, and the French nationality of the undertakers, this seems nearly equivalent to an unwillingness on the part of our bankers to back new American enterprise for entry into the aluminum industry. The plant of the Southern Aluminium Company could not be removed to Europe, and it was as safe as any other domestic establishment from foreign depredations. . . .

In the possession of the Aluminum Company of America the plant was pushed to rapid completion in order to meet the now bounding demands of the belligerents. The war called into being immense extensions of plant and yielded large returns with which to finance them. During 1915 and 1916 the company spent at least twenty million dollars in expansion and practically doubled its capacity. Investment jumped from a little under fifty millions in 1915 to a little over ninety millions in 1918. Apparently no other attempts to enter the field were made until after the war, by which time the size and strength of the Aluminum Company had been appreciably enhanced.[12]

Professor Wallace suggests that neglect of the aluminum industry by investment bankers during the 1909-1918 decade indicates that there must have been weighty deterrent elements.[13] "One wonders," he says, "whether the mere prestige of the Mellon group has not influenced the situation." He concludes, however, that non-appearance of competition for Alcoa during this period mainly resulted from failure of United States law to require publication of data covering capacity, production, consumption, and financial condition. Alcoa was thus enabled to withhold basic information which promoters and bankers needed in order to exercise their social function of directing capital and enterprise into channels where they would meet consumer demands.

From 1918 to 1925 there were two additional instances in which it seemed that groups with adequate resources were about to undertake the manufacture of aluminum in competition with Alcoa, but in both cases they also sold out to the Mellon interests before reaching the stage of actual production.[14] The first of these episodes was one involving the Uihlein family of Milwaukee, owners of the Schlitz Brewing Company. Shortly after the armistice was signed in 1918 the Uihleins initiated attempts to secure an adequate supply of bauxite ore in British Guiana, and later in Dutch Guiana. Due to a series of difficulties, including a prolonged legal battle with the Demerara Bauxite Company, a subsidiary of Alcoa, the Uihleins' agent was unable to secure for them title to these deposits until 1923. In the meantime the Uihleins, who had planned to use Niagara Falls power, found that sufficient energy was not available from that source at a satisfactory price. The outcome was that in 1925 they sold their bauxite deposits to Alcoa, the Carborundum Company, and the Acheson Graphite Company, each of these three Mellon companies taking a one-third interest.

The second serious threat of competition for Alcoa in the decade immediately following the first World War was a case in which the principal figures were George D. Haskell, president of the Bausch Machine Tool Company, and James B. Duke, who until 1912 had been president of the American Tobacco Company. Haskell was interested in securing an independent supply of aluminum for his company and Duke in finding a profitable use for the large water power development which he was contemplating on the Saguenay River in the Canadian province of Quebec. Haskell later claimed that he and Duke in 1924 had reached an oral understanding whereby they would organize an aluminum manufacturing company to use the Saguenay water power. In June, 1925, however, Haskell learned that Duke had made a deal with Alcoa. This was in the nature of a merger in which Duke got $16,000,000 par value of Alcoa preferred stock, which was one-ninth of the amount outstanding, plus 15 per cent of the common stock, in exchange for his Saguenay water power. He died three months after this merger was consummated and Haskell resorted to legal action, in 1928 receiving an award of $8,000,000 damages against the Duke estate. He lost this case on appeal, however, the higher court holding that there was insufficient evidence to prove that a contract existed between Duke and Haskell.

The monopoly continued until 1940, at which point annual production of primary aluminum in North America amounted to about 286,000 tons worth $115,000,000, almost 2000 times its 1893 tonnage, and practically all of that increase went to Alcoa and the Canadian company which it controlled. In 1940 the Mellon interests' 47-year rule of the aluminum industry came to an end. World War II demand for the metal prompted the Government to induce and finance new production, and this brought into the field on a large scale the Reynolds Metals Company and Kaiser Aluminum and Chemical Corporation which together in 1956 accounted for about 38 per cent of this continent's total production of aluminum.

In the fall of 1941 was concluded what, as reported by Alva Johnston in the *New Yorker*,[15] was probably the longest trial in the history of the world, namely Assistant Attorney General Thurman Arnold's suit against Alcoa charging violation of the Sherman Act against monopolizing.[16] The trial lasted for more than two years of almost daily court sessions and the printed record occupied 480 volumes containing 15,000,000 words, the total cost of the action being about $2,500,000. Judge Caffey's opinion was in scale with the rest of the proceedings, having been given orally from the bench over a period of nine days, and occupying 250 printed pages. The Government lost on all of about 140 points. After the trial Judge Caffey retired to Alabama for a well-earned rest but Arnold immediately summoned him back to New York for the purpose of whipping together his 200,000-word opinion into final form. Arnold was in such a hurry to get on with the action that, according to Johnston, he even "asked permission to appeal the decision in its rough draft instead of waiting for the finished product. Taking this plea under advisement, Judge Caffey said, 'If there is any legal way for me to get rid of this case, I'll do it so quick that it'll make your head swim.'"

On appeal the Government met with more success. In March, 1945, Judges L. Hand, Swan, and A. N. Hand reversed the lower court, ordering a decree which enjoined "price squeeze" practices of Alcoa, and also enjoined further cartel arrangements overseas.[17] The Government's 14-year monopoly suit against Alcoa was finally brought to an end on January 16, 1951, by Judge Knox's decree [18] under terms of which nine principal Alcoa shareholders were required to divest themselves of their stock ownership, either in Alcoa or in Aluminium Limited. They were given 10 years from May 1, 1951, to dispose of their stock. Actually, by October, 1955, most of these men had sold two-thirds of their Aluminium Limited stock,[19] only one of the group, E. K. Davis, retired president of Aluminium Limited, having elected to retain the latter and sell his interest in Alcoa.[20]

Almost two-thirds of the world's total of primary aluminum originates in North America where 2,300,000 short tons were produced in 1956, an increase of 20 per cent in two years. About 33 per cent of 1956 North American production was accounted for by Alcoa and 27 per cent by Alcan (Aluminum Company of Canada),[21] practically all of the balance being divided about equally between Reynolds and Kaiser.

In addition to the appearance of competition within the aluminum industry there are also new metals which may some day challenge the supremacy of aluminum itself in the light-metals field. One of these is magnesium which first made its appearance commercially in this country only 43 years ago and which enjoyed a great boom in production during the second World War, principally in connection with airplane construction and pyrotechnics.[22] Its use for civilian purposes is increasing rapidly but in 1956 the tonnage of primary magnesium produced in North America was only slightly more than one-thirtieth the production of primary aluminum. In the third quarter of 1957 its price per pound was about one-third higher than that of aluminum but it weighs about two-thirds as much, being 112 pounds per cubic foot as compared with 175 pounds for aluminum and 493 pounds for steel. Magnesium, a silvery white metal, gains strength through alloying and is more malleable than aluminum, its principal disadvantages being low resistance to corrosion and inflammability. It only ignites, however, when in the form of a powder or fine ribbon, or through application of very intense heat. It is the third most plentiful metal found in the earth's crust, being exceeded only by aluminum and iron.

Magnesium can be extracted by a variety of processes from a number of different sources including magnesite and dolomite ores, brine wells, and even sea water. During 1957 by far the most important producer of this metal in North America was the Dow Chemical Company. Relatively small amounts were being manufactured by the Aluminum Company of Canada, Dominion Magnesium in Canada, Titanium Metals Corporation in Nevada, and a U.S. Government plant in Connecticut. It is thought, however, that Dow currently accounts for about 80 per cent of all magnesium manufactured in North America. This company produces magnesium from brine at various points in Michigan and from sea water at Freeport, Texas. It employs an electrolytic process whereby pure magnesium is reduced from magnesium chloride which has been produced by a complex chemical process employing brine or sea water and oyster shells from the Gulf of Mexico. Natural gas is used in Texas to heat the kilns, evaporators, and driers, and to generate the electricity for electrolysis. It will be seen in Chart 2, Appendix A, that growth in commercial production of magnesium in North America during its first 42 years from 1915 to 1956 roughly parallels that of aluminum in the 42 years from 1887 to 1928.

Another new metal, thus far in its commercial infancy, is titanium. Much stronger than aluminum, and tougher than many steel alloys though considerably lighter, it also has the important property of retaining its strength at elevated temperatures and is very resistant to corrosion. Its present uses are primarily in the aircraft and military missile fields. Titanium was first produced commercially as a pure metal in 1948. This may seem surprising in view of the fact that it is the ninth most abundant element in the earth's crust, being exceeded among commercial metals only by aluminum, iron, and magnesium. It comprises a larger proportion of known terrestrial matter than copper, lead, and zinc combined, and is from five to ten times more abundant than such well-known non-metals as phosphorus and sulphur. Its price per pound in the third quarter of 1957, however, was about twenty times that of aluminum, mainly due to the fact that its occurrence is more scattered than that of the common commercial metals, thus making extraction more expensive. If its cost can be reduced substantially it may take a very significant place in the industrial world.

There are also possibilities in the development of ceramic or plastic products, a field which was greatly stimulated by research during the second World War. In May, 1957, for example, the Corning Glass Works announced that as a result of defense research it had developed a glass called pyroceram, reported to be lighter than aluminum and harder and cheaper than stainless steel. The first use of pyroceram will be for missiles but it is quite possible that before long this or kindred products may to a considerable extent replace metal parts now employed in the manufacture of many articles widely used by civilians.

NOTES

[1] Carr, *op. cit.*, p. 40.

[2] *Ibid.*, p. 47.

[3] *Ibid.*, p. 44. See also United States *vs.* Alcoa *et al.*, D.C.S.D., New York, 1941, 44 Fed. Sup. 97.

[4] United States *vs.* Alcoa *et al.*, D.C.S.D., New York, 1941, 44 Fed. Sup. 97.

[5] Harvey O'Connor, *Mellon's Millions* (New York: John Day Co., 1933), p. 83.

[6] Wallace, *op. cit.*, Appendix C.

[7] Moody's Manual for 1910 reports 1907 balance sheet items of the Aluminum Company of America as the latest available, the credit side only being reported, as follows: common stock $3,200,000, six per cent preferred stock $600,000, accounts and bills payable $2,892,749, profit and loss, $6,497,819. No mention is made of any funded debt. Similarly, Moody's Manual for 1905 lists the Pittsburgh Reduction Company's capital structure as consisting of $3,200,000 in common stock and $600,000 in preferred stock, no funded debt being listed.

[8] Carr, *op. cit.*, p. 48.

[9] U.S. Patent Office hearing, A. H. Cowles *vs.* Franz A. Rody, October 23, 1916, p. 3.

[10] Statements from here to end of paragraph are based on Wallace, *op. cit.*, pp. 103-8.

[11] On January 1, 1907, Pittsburgh Reduction Company changed its name to Aluminum Company of America (Alcoa).

[12] Wallace, *op. cit.*, pp. 115-18.

[13] Wallace, *op. cit.*, p. 151.

[14] Information regarding these two cases is from Wallace, *op. cit.*, pp. 129-37.

[15] Alva Johnston, "Thurman Arnold's Biggest Case," *New Yorker*, January 24, 1942, pp. 25-31, and January 31, 1942, pp. 40-46.

[16] U.S.D.C., New York, N.D., 1941, 44 Fed. Sup. 97.

[17] U.S.C.C.A. 2nd, 1945, 148 Fed. 2nd 416.

[18] U.S.D.C., New York, S.D., 1951, 91 Fed. Sup. 333.

[19] William B. Harris, "The Splendid Retreat of Alcoa," *Fortune*, October, 1955, p. 118.

[20] See terms of monopoly suit settlement described under Aluminium Limited in *Moody's Industrial Manual*—1955.

[21] Alcan is the abbreviated title used to designate the Aluminum Company of Canada which is the Canadian operating company owned by the holding company, Aluminium, Limited.

[22] Information regarding magnesium in this paragraph is taken mainly from Engle, Gregory, and Mossé, *Aluminum* (Chicago: Richard D. Irwin, Inc., 1945), pp. 362-86.

Chapter X

Conclusion

Development of the modern process for production of aluminum depended upon the accumulation of knowledge contributed over a span of about 100 years by many scientists working in electrochemistry and allied fields. The key discoveries included Volta's invention of the electric battery in 1800 which led to experiments in electrolysis by Davy and others during the early part of the nineteenth century, and to the first electrolytic production of aluminum by Deville and Bunsen in 1854. The fact that molten cryolite would dissolve alumina was noted by Deville in 1859 and by many others during the succeeding 25 years. Patents were taken out in Europe on ideas originated by Le Chatelier in 1861, Varin in 1883, and Boguski in 1884, all for processes which covered the production of aluminum or its alloys by electrolysis of various compounds including mixtures of alumina with molten cryolite. These processes, however, were not commercially successful, in part because they employed external combustion heat to fuse the ore. Development of the electric dynamo by Faraday, Siemens, Wheatstone, Gramme, and others progressed over the period from 1831 to about 1878 when it first began to be used commercially. At that point it remained for Bradley and the Cowles brothers, through invention of the electric furnace in the early 1880s, to provide the final contribution needed in order to complete the groundwork essential for development of the modern aluminum process.

The Cowles brothers were the first to employ the modern process of electrolyzing alumina dissolved in cryolite which had been reduced to a molten state in an electric furnace. They did this in experiments conducted during the spring and early summer of 1887 which, however, were inconclusive because of impurities present in the ore. Hall and Héroult in 1889 were the first to employ the modern process commercially and this presumably accounts for the widespread impression that they originated it in spite of the fact that, like their predecessors Le Chatelier, Varin, and Boguski, they did not even suggest in their original patents that the cryolite bath might be fused by internal electric heat.

At a meeting of the American Electrochemical Society in Philadelphia during April, 1927, Junius D. Edwards, a member of the Alcoa research department, presented a paper on the history of aluminum in which he restated the widely accepted proposition that discovery of the modern process for producing aluminum was made by his company's inventor, Hall, on February 23, 1886. This claim by Edwards was challenged by James T. Newton who had worked in the United States Patent Office for 31 years from 1891 to 1921, during the last five years of which he had held the top post as Commissioner of Patents (Hartford, *op. cit.,* pp. 10-12). In replying to Edwards, Commissioner Newton stated that Hall, in an interference proceeding in the United States patent office some time prior to the issue of his first patent in 1889, was granted an award of priority over Héroult on the broad issue, "electrolysis of a solution of alumina in a fused fluoride salt of aluminum," but that both applicants were showing the process carried out in externally-heated crucibles employing less watt energy per pound of aluminum than would have been required to fuse the ore by internal electric heat, and that the issue was not so worded as to describe the modern process for producing aluminum.

In writings describing the industry's origin the version generally given has been that Hall discovered the modern process in his woodshed experiment on February 23, 1886, and that he established the validity of this claim by a clear-cut court victory over the Cowles brothers when Judge Taft in 1893 held that the Cowles Company had been infringing his patent. No reference has generally been made to the fact that the decision of Judge Taft was rendered doubtful by Judge Wing's reopening the case to receive evidence as to whether Hall's process or contributions of the Cowles brothers really brought about the successful production of aluminum.

It is difficult to understand how writers in commenting on the industry's early history could have overlooked the indisputable fact that the courts ultimately held the Cowles-Bradley internal heating method to be a central and crucial factor in success of the modern process. There can be no doubt that Hall utilized someone else's electric-furnace idea. This is attested to by the 1903 decree of the Circuit Court of Appeals in New York which entered a judgment against his company, reported as amounting to nearly $3,000,000, for infringement of the Cowles-owned Bradley patent on the electric furnace, and also by the fact that the furnace universally employed in the aluminum industry to this day is basically the same as that which the Cowles brothers invented, and were the first to use commercially, more than 72 years ago.

The Pittsburgh Reduction Company, predecessor to Alcoa, became established in its monopolistic position through infringement of patents owned by its only competitor, and through a questionable (and judicially questioned) lower court decision which closed down the plant of that competitor for 10 years. The fact that the Cowles Company was never able thereafter to resume production of aluminum, and also that Hall ultimately received a $30,000,000 reward for his invention, misled the public into believing that he had won a conclusive victory on the issue of who originated the modern process.

It would be interesting to know what Taft's decision would have been if he had known all the facts finally disclosed in the trial of the Cowles Company's suit charging the Pittsburgh Reduction Company with infringement of the Bradley patent. He might have reached a different conclusion had he realized that the Hall process was a failure commercially until the Bradley-Cowles internal-heating feature was adopted. At least Judge Wing had such a possibility in mind when he reopened the original case to admit evidence on these matters. If Taft's decision had gone the other way there might never have been an aluminum monopoly. In that case, instead of the Cowles brothers and their electric furnace being consigned to oblivion, Hall might have been forgotten. This, too, would have been unfair. From the facts which are known it seems clear that each of the young men, Hall, Héroult, Bradley, and the Cowles brothers, should have received credit for taking an important part in developing the process which constitutes the foundation of the modern multi-billion dollar aluminum industry. Surely there was glory enough in that sensational episode for it to have been shared by them all.

Charts Showing Aluminum Production and Prices in Relation to Other Metals

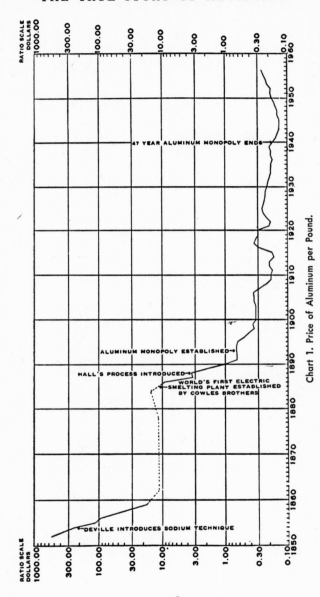

Chart 1. Price of Aluminum per Pound.

128

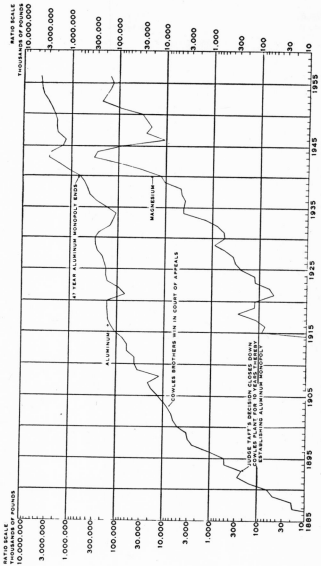

Chart 2. Primary Light Metals Production in North America.

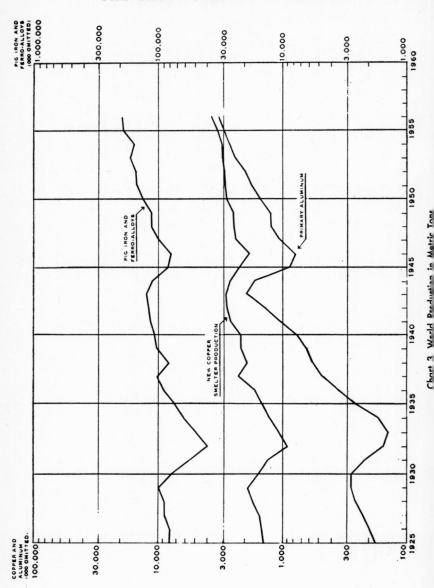

Chart 3. World Production in Metric Tons

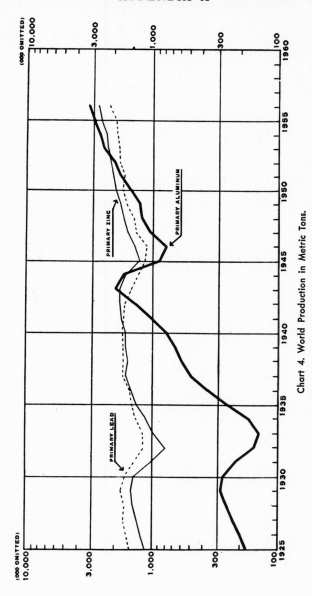

Chart 4. World Production in Metric Tons.

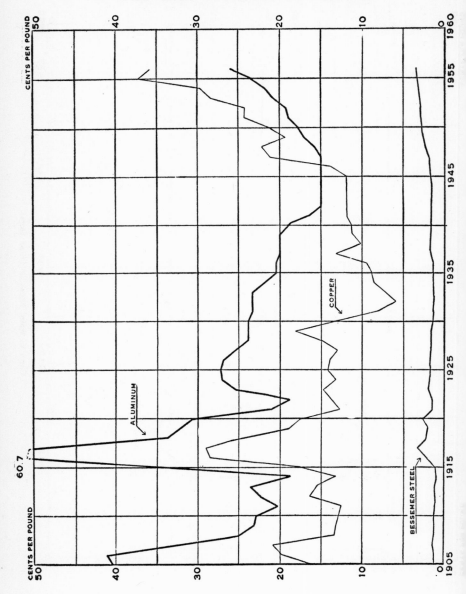

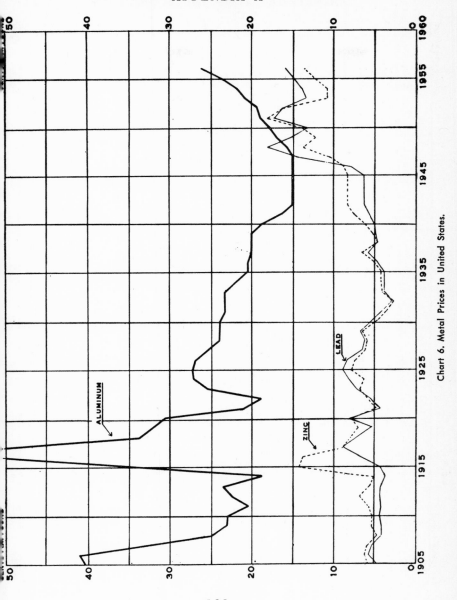

Chart 6. Metal Prices in United States.

Drawings and Specifications of 11 Patents Discussed in Text

LE CHATELIER'S PIONEERING SOLUBLE ANODE PATENT

This British patent No. 1214 was issued on November 13, 1861, to Thomas Bell as agent for Louis Le Chatelier of Paris, a co-worker with Henri St. Claire Deville. It includes the proposal that anodes composed of alumina and carbon be immersed in molten cryolite and that aluminum be extracted from the mixture by electrolysis and plated onto metal surfaces. This may be verified by reference to paragraphs 5 and 6 of the specification where, among various alternatives suggested, are anodes consisting of alumina and carbon and a bath composed of cryolite. The alumina in the anodes presumably would dissolve upon contact with the molten cryolite. The following is the specification of this Le Chatelier patent:

To all to whom these presents shall come, I, Thomas Bell, of Usworth House, Gateshead, in the County of Durham, Ironmaster, send greeting.

Whereas Her most Excellent Majesty Queen Victoria,

by Her Letters Patent, bearing date the Thirteenth day of May, in the year of our Lord One thousand eight hundred and sixty-one, in the twenty-fourth year of Her reign, did, for Herself, Her heirs and successors, give and grant unto me, the said Thomas Bell, Her special license that I, the said Thomas Bell, my executors, administrators, and assigns, or such others as I, the said Thomas Bell, my executors, administrators, and assigns, should at any time agree with, and no others, from time to time and at all times thereafter during the term therein expressed, should and lawfully might make, use, exercise, and vend, within the United Kingdom of Great Britain and Ireland, the Channel Islands, and Isle of Man, an Invention for "Improvements in the Decomposition of the Compounds of Aluminium and in Coating Metals with Aluminium or its Alloys," being a communication from abroad by Louis Le Chatelier, of Paris, in the Empire of France, upon the condition (amongst others) that I, the said Thomas Bell, by an instrument in writing under my hand and seal, should particularly describe and ascertain the nature of the said Invention, and in what manner the same was to be performed, and cause the same to be filed in the Great Seal Patent Office within six calendar months next and immediately after the date of the said Letters Patent.

Now know ye, that I, the said Thomas Bell, do hereby declare the nature of the said Invention, and in what manner the same is to be performed, to be particularly described and ascertained in and by the following statement (that is to say):—

This Invention consists in effecting the decomposition of the compounds of aluminium (for instance, the double chloride of aluminium and sodium) by the agency of galvanic electricity, and also in coating metals with aluminium

135

by the same agency. By means of this process I am enabled to convert the surface of copper (for instance) into aluminium bronze.

The bath is composed of the double chloride of aluminium and sodium in an anhydrous state, and which is kept melted at a temperature of about three hundred and sixty degrees Fahrenheit. The negative electrode is represented by the piece of copper or other metal which it is intended to cover or coat with aluminium. The soluble positive electrode may be of aluminium, but there is economy in using a composition of carbon and anhydrous alumina. This composition is compressed in a mould of a cylindrical or other suitable form, then calcined in a close vessel before being used. This process produces the chloride of aluminium, with the chlorine, which is disengaged by the action of the electric current. A mixture of alumina and coal tar moulded and calcined answers very well. A positive electrode made from the carbonaceous matter deposited in the interior of gas retorts may also be employed. When a positive electrode composed of carbon mixed or not with alumina is employed, small pieces of carbon become detached during the operation and soil the bath; to remedy this the electrode may be enclosed within a porous earthen vessel, which is placed in the bath containing the double chloride. The bath, instead of being composed only of the double chloride of aluminium and sodium, may consist of a mixture of this chloride with cryolite, which mixture is fusible at a dull red heat.

Cryolite alone may be used, but it has the inconvenience of melting at a high temperature. A deposit of aluminium on copper having been effected, if the piece be heated at a suitable temperature, the alumina and copper combine and the surface of the piece of metal will be converted into a bronze of aluminium.

Having now described this Invention of improvements in the decomposition of the compounds of aluminium and in coating metals with aluminium or its alloys, and having explained the manner of carrying the same into effect, I claim as the Invention secured to me by Letters Patent as aforesaid, the mode herein set forth of effecting the decomposition of the compounds of aluminium and of coating metals with aluminium or its alloys. I claim particularly the employment for the above mentioned purposes of galvanic electricity in the manner above described.

In witness whereof, I, the said Thomas Bell, have hereunto set my hand and seal, the Twelfth day of November, in the year of our Lord One thousand eight hundred and sixty-one.

THOMAS BELL

BRADLEY'S IMPORTANT PATENT

This United States Patent Number 468,148, although applied for on February 23, 1883, was not issued until February 2, 1892. It covers electrolysis of aluminum ore by the same current which fuses it by internal electric heat. This patent, entitled "Process of Separating Aluminum," was purchased by the Cowles brothers from Bradley, along with his other inventions pertaining to this subject, in the spring of 1885. The Cowles Company used it as the basis for an infringement suit which, after many years of litigation, it won in the United States Circuit Court of Appeals in New York on October 20, 1903, from the Pittsburgh Reduction Company, predecessor to the Aluminum Company of America. The following are the drawings and specification of this Bradley patent:

THE TRUE STORY OF ALUMINUM

TO ALL WHOM IT MAY CONCERN:

Be it known that I, CHARLES S. BRADLEY, of the city, county, and State of New York, have invented a new and useful Improvement in processes for Separating Aluminium, of which the following is a specification.

My invention relates to a process of effecting by the electric current the separation or dissociation of aluminium from its ores or compounds, or the decomposition in a similar manner of other like highly-refractory metallic compounds of which aluminium may be considered a type and which have been classed together by reason of the great difficulty in their reduction.

Hitherto this process has been carried on by subjecting the fused ore to the action of the current in a crucible or other refractory vessel placed in a heating-furnace where the temperature is sufficiently high to keep the ore in a melted condition; but the greatest difficulty is encountered in preventing the destruction of the crucible with this mode of working the process, for it has been found that, in the case of cryolite especially, which is a double fluoride of aluminium and sodium, the fused ore unites or fluxes with the crucible itself, and that the gas liberated in the process of reduction (fluorine gas) attacks the material of which the crucible is composed, and the consequence is that the crucible is quickly destroyed. This destructive fluxing action takes place to a greater or less extent in treating almost any material, and is greatly aggravated by the fact that the crucible is subjected to heat from without; but even in the case of materials which do not exert a fluxing action the mere mechanical action of the external heat is sufficient to make it almost impossible to prevent the cracking of the crucibles.

The main object of my invention, therefore, is to dispense with the external application of heat to the ore in order to keep it fused. In order to accomplish this object, I employ an electric current of greater strength or intensity than what would be required to produce the electrolytic decomposition alone, and I maintain the ore or other substance in a state of fusion by the heat developed by the passage of the current through the melted mass, so that by my invention the electric current is employed to perform two distinct functions, one of these being to keep the ore melted by having a portion of its electrical energy converted into heat by the electrical resistance offered by the fused ore, and the other being to effect the desired electrolytic decomposition, by which means the heat, being produced in the ore itself, is concentrated at exactly the point where it is required to keep the ore in a state of fusion.

Another feature of my invention consists in dispensing with the crucible for holding the ore and in employing a body or heap of the ore itself to constitute the vessel or cell in which the reduction takes place which is not destroyed by the chemical action of the fused ore and the gas liberated, and which therefore admits of the process being perfectly continuous, nothing being required but the charging of fresh ore as fast as the reduction goes on, either from without or from the sides or walls of the heap itself.

To enable others to carry out my process, I will proceed to describe as applied in one particular case to the extraction of aluminium from its ore cryolite.

In the accompanying drawings, Fig. 1 is a sectional view of a pile of ore with the electrodes in position in the basin and connected to a source of electric current. Figs. 2, 3, and 4 are modified arrangements.

Upon a hearth of brick 1 or other suitable material is piled a heap or body 2 of the ore, more or less pulverized, in the shape of a truncated cone, and a cavity or basin 3 is excavated in the top of the heap to contain the fused portion of the ore which is to be treated electrolytically. In order to

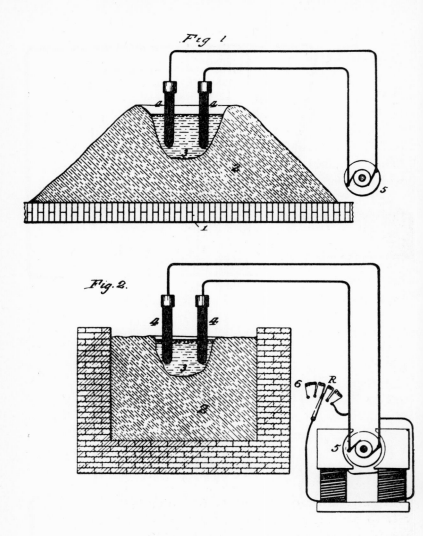

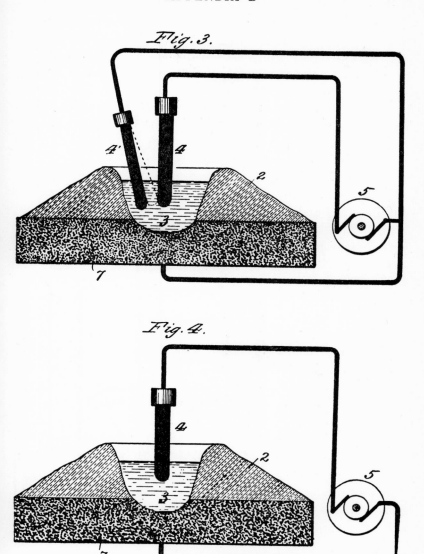

Fig. 3.

Fig. 4.

fuse the ore at the start, I take two electrodes 4 of a suitable material, such as already used in like processes where fusion has been effected by an external furnace and connected, respectively, to the two poles of dynamo-electric machine 5 or other sources of current, bring the said electrodes into contact, separate them sufficiently to produce an electric arc, and then thrust them into the ore lying at the bottom of the cavity or basin, where the ore soon fuses by the heat of the arc and becomes a conducting electrolyte, through which the current from the electrodes continues to flow. The arc of course ceases to exist as soon as there is a conducting-liquid—the fused ore—between the electrodes, and the passage of the current then takes place through the fused ore by conduction and the heat is produced as it is in an incandescent lamp. The arc is merely used to melt the ore in the beginning and the ore is kept melted by incandescence, so to speak, the metallic aluminium being gradually deposited at the cathode and the fluorine gas being set free at the anode so long as the ore is maintained, in a state of fusion. As soon as the action is properly started the electrodes should be moved a little farther apart, in order that the metal set free at the cathode shall not form a short circuit between the electrodes or be attacked by the fluorine set free at the anode.

I have spoken several times of fluorine being set free, although I am aware that it is considered to be almost impossible to isolate that element. I use the term "fluorine" merely for convenience, meaning thereby whatever is set free at the anode, which may be fluorine or some compound of fluorine, with the substance composing the anode, moisture of the air, &c. As a matter of fact, when the process is worked fumes arise at the anode; but the anode is not attacked or eaten away very rapidly, provided it is made of pure carbon, such as gas-retort carbon, which I prefer in preference to carbon containing silica or alumina.

In working my process I employ, as I have already stated, an electric current sufficiently powerful not only to effect the electrolytic decomposition of the ore treated, but also to develop by its passage the heat required to keep the ore fused. I have found that by using an electric current about twice as strong as would be employed to perform a given amount of electrolytic work in the ordinary way in externally-heated crucibles, I am enabled to keep the ore fused according to my invention without the application of any external heat whatever.

For the purpose of perfectly managing and controlling my process, I have my electric generator or source of current so arranged that the strength of the electrolytic current may be properly regulated and the mass of ore thereby kept at the proper temperature. The most efficient way to accomplish this is to raise or lower the electro-motive force of the generator by any of the well-known methods employed—for example, in incandescent electric lighting. One of the well-known methods for accomplishing this is illustrated in Fig. 2, and consists in the employment of an adjustable resistance R in the field-circuit of the generator. By these means I am enabled to dispense with the necessity of keeping the ore in a fused state by the application of heat from without through the walls of the refractory vessel and to concentrate the heat required for this purpose just where it is needed between the two electrodes, and by the use of a vessel or cavity formed of the ore itself I avoid its destruction by the action of the melted ore and by the gas or acid set free during decomposition.

The body of unfused ore may either be formed into an unconfined pile, as in Fig. 1, or it may be contained in a receptacle or box 6 of any desired shape, so as practically to form a tank or holder lined with the ore itself, as in Fig. 2. Such a lining will prevent the destruction of the holder, and the process may go on indefinitely without interruption. As fast as the reduction proceeds and the metal is set free fresh ore may be supplied to the bath and the metal removed therefrom, if desired, in any desired way. The fresh ore may be introduced on the top by shoveling it in or by means of a hopper, which may be regulated to feed the ore at a constant rate, or it may be introduced intermittently by hand. The metal set free may likewise be drawn off, as frequently as desirable, by ladling it out by hand or by boring a tap-hole through to the molten metal and allowing it to run off.

It is evident that various forms of furnace and built of various materials may be employed without departing from my invention. Instances of two such modifications are illustrated by Figs. 3 and 4. In Fig. 3 the body 2 of ore is heaped upon a slab of carbon 7, which is connected to one of the poles of the dynamo-electric machine 5. The electrodes 4 and 4' are first brought together and inserted in the basin 3 into the contained ore and then separated to form the arc, as previously described, and when the heat has melted down a portion of the ore so as to form a conductor the electrode 4' may be withdrawn and the operation thereafter continued between the electrode 4 and the carbon slab 7. In Fig. 4 the arrangement is the same, except that the electrode 4' is omitted, and in this instance the operation is started by first establishing contact between the electrode 4 and the carbon slab 7, and then the former is withdrawn as soon as a sufficient quantity of fused ore is present to conduct the current and effect the required results.

I have described my process as preferably carried on by employing a body of the ore itself to form the basin or receptacle in which the electrodes are situated, between which the current flows through the ore for heating and electrolyzing the same. That specific invention, however, is not claimed herein, since it forms the subject-matter of Patent No. 464,933, dated December 8, 1891.

My present invention is not limited to the specific character of the receptacle nor the specific arrangements of the electrodes.

What I claim as my invention is as follows:

1. The process of separating or dissociating metals from their highly-refractory ores or compounds, non-conductors in an unfused state, of which the ores and compounds of aluminium are a type, which consists in fusing the refractory ore or compound progressively by a source of heat concentrated directly upon it rather than by an external furnace and as it becomes fused effecting electrolysis by passing an electric current therethrough between terminals which are maintained in circuit with the fused bath, whereby the process is rendered continuous, substantially as set forth.

2. The continuous process of separating or dissociating metals from aluminous or like highly-refractory ores or compounds, non-conductors in an unfused state, which consists in progressively fusing the refractory ore or compound and as it becomes fused electrolyzing it by passing an electric current therethrough of sufficient volume to continue and maintain the fusion and effect electrolysis and adding fresh material from time to time to preserve the bath constant, as set forth.

3. The process of reducing metals from that class of highly-refractory ores and compounds, non-conductors in an unfused state, of which the ores and compounds of aluminium are a type, which consists in fusing a portion of the refractory ore or compound to be treated, in establishing an electric current through said fused portion, and by such current producing simultaneously progressive fusion of such ore or compound and continuous electrolysis of the same as fused.

4. The process of separating or dissociating aluminium from its ores or compounds, consisting in fusing and maintaining the fusion and electrolytically decomposing the ore or compound by the passage of the electric current therethrough, substantially as set forth.

5. The continuous process of separating or dissociating aluminium from its ores or compounds, consisting in fusing and maintaining the fusion and electrolytically decomposing the ore or compound by the passage of the electric current therethrough and charging the bath with fresh quantities of the ore or compound as the reduction proceeds, substantially as set forth.

6. The process of separating or dissociating aluminium from its ores or compounds, consisting in fusing and maintaining the fusion and electrolytically decomposing the ore or compound by the passage of the electric current therethrough and regulating the strength of said current in accordance with the requirements of the fused mass, substantially as set forth.

CHARLES S. BRADLEY

VARIN'S SOLUBLE ANODE PATENT

This French Patent Number 155,333 was taken out on May 10, 1883, by Julien Edward Varin, a chemist residing at Epinal (Vosges), France. It describes a process in which soluble anodes composed of alumina and carbon are immersed in a fused bath which may be a double fluoride of aluminum and sodium (cryolite) as stated in paragraph 9 of the specification. The alumina in the anodes would dissolve upon contact with the cryolite bath. Aluminum is then extracted from the mixture by electrolysis and plated onto the cathode composed of coarse sheets of aluminum, these sheets and the de-

146

posited aluminum being then all melted down together. The following is a translation of the specification of Varin's French patent:

When Deville, in 1854, presented to the Academy of Sciences an ingot of aluminum, which he had obtained by decomposing the chloride of that metal by the battery, he said: "One can obtain aluminum by that means as well as by sodium; but, evidently because of the small equivalent of aluminum in relation to the zinc, that method gives to the metal a rather high cost price." To-day the magneto and dynamo electric machines furnish to electro-chemistry their powerful and economical currents. They are the apparatus which I have thought to employ for the commercial production of aluminum.

My process is summed up in the decomposition by the electricity furnished by these machines of the melted chloride of aluminum. The aluminum deposits at the negative electrode and the chlorine separates at the positive anode. Here are the details of the means employed:

The simple chloride volatilizing before it melts cannot be employed alone, it is the double chloride of aluminum and sodium which serves the best for the composition of the electrolytic bath; fusible at 185°, fixed even at a red heat, when it is fused it is of a perfect fluidity and presents but a feeble resistance to electricity. It becomes easy to purify the bath from all foreign metallic matters which it may contain by the current itself, since these substances precipitate with the first layers of aluminum which deposit. It suffices to insert a provisional negative electrode which is replaced by another as soon as the metal which deposits appears to be pure.

To maintain the composition of the bath constant, one should add to it from time to time, some of the simple chloride, for the purpose of replacing that which has been decomposed by the current, and should operate in a closed vase, in order to collect the chlorine and direct it by a tube into the retort where the chloride is prepared, but I have found a much more practical means in the employment of a soluble anode. That anode is formed of an intimate mixture of alumina and carbon; the chlorine instead of becoming free attacks the alumina, regenerating the chloride decomposed, while the carbon combining with the oxygen of the alumina produces a regular escape of oxide of carbon, which it is easier to get rid of.

The alumina employed for the preparation of these anodes should be as pure as possible; it is mixed with ten per cent. of purified wood charcoal in powder and a little water, then one adds enough tar to agglomerate the whole, which is triturated so as to obtain a perfectly homogeneous mass. It is then moulded into rectangular plates by means of a power press, which expels the water previously introduced into the mixture in order to work it. The dense plate which is removed from the press is placed to dry in the open air. After drying the plates are placed standing in pots filled with carbon dust, being separated by powdered carbon to avoid their adhering and becoming deformed. The well covered pots are heated in a reverberatory furnace until the tar is completely decomposed. The aluminous carbon thus obtained is hard, sonorous, and conducts electricity perfectly, but it is very hygrometric so that there is an advantage in using it on removing it from the pots while it is still hot.

The negative electrodes may be of retort carbon, but I have found it convenient and also economical to make use of sheets of aluminum, coarsely flattened, which it is not necessary to separate from the metal, which is deposited in thick layers upon its surface, but the whole is melted together.

By employing a sheet of copper for the negative electrode,

which is melted with its deposits of aluminum, there is obtained aluminum bronze of different qualities according to the quantity of metal which has been deposited, which may always be regulated.

The bath of chloride is maintained in fusion in sheet iron pots internally enameled, heated by a special hearth which supplies the necessary quantity of heat to that which is furnished by the waste flames of the reverberatory furnace. These pots are closed by a cover, in order to maintain the bath in proper condition and also to allow the carrying off by a tube of the oxide of carbon.

The process which I have described is applicable to the double fluoride of aluminum and sodium, rendered more fusible by the suitable addition of chloride. One may further, strictly, employ the bromide of aluminum; also I reserve to myself in the application of my process to employ those of these compounds which I may judge to be suitable to substitute for the double chloride which I have chosen in the description.

According to the experiments which I have made with a Gramme electro-plating machine, type No. 1, I estimate that aluminum can be produced by this process at a price costing at least ten times less than by the process with sodium. I believe that there is here a commercial result of incontestable importance.

Signed: VARIN

BOGUSKI'S BRITISH PATENT

This British patent No. 3090 was issued to Anthony Zdziarski as agent for Joseph Boguski of Warsaw, then a part of Russia. The provisional specification is dated February 11, 1884, and the complete specification November 8, 1884.

The Cowles brothers sent an agent to Russia who in January, 1887, purchased for them from Boguski the rights to his various inventions including this patent. According to Alfred H. Cowles the meaning of this patent is obscured by the fact that it is a faulty translation from the Polish, Boguski's native tongue, the true nature of his idea being disclosed in paragraph 5, and in paragraphs 7 and 8 if the two latter are read together as one paragraph. In the first line of paragraph 8 "mixture of an oxide of aluminum" is to be interpreted as being a mixture of alumina and cryolite, and in arriving at the real meaning of the patent consideration should also be given to the fact that the only compound mentioned containing fluorine is cryolite which is mentioned five distinct times in this short specification. It has been contended that the patent, when considered in this way, covers the production of aluminum bronze by electrolysis of alumina dissolved in cryolite and that it can be made to cover the production of pure aluminum simply by substituting a carbon cathode for one composed of molten copper. The Cowles brothers also were influenced in their opinion of the importance of this patent by first-hand reports which they received of metal produced by electrolysis of alumina dissolved in cryolite in demonstrations of the process conducted by Boguski's agent, Zdziarski, at the London Industrial exhibition in 1884 [1] The complete specification is as follows:

I, Anthony Zdziarski of Brest-Litowsk, Russia, Engineer, but temporarily residing at the Queen's Hotel St. Martins-le-Grand in the City of London do hereby declare the nature of said Invention for "Improvements in Obtaining Aluminium Bronze" and in what manner the same is to be per-

[1] Electric Smelting & Aluminum Co. *vs.* Pittsburgh Reduction Co., C.C.W.D., New York, 1901, Complainant's Record, pp. 106-7, 125, 213-15, 404-6 (decision reported 111 Fed. 742).

formed to be particularly described and ascertained in and by the following statement:—

According to this Invention Aluminium Bronze is obtained from melted cryolite with a suitable flux or from mixtures of other compound of aluminium and a suitable flux, by means of a current of electricity, copper brass or other metals being employed in a melted state for the cathode.

And in order that the said Invention may be properly understood, I will proceed to describe a system mode or manner, in or under which the said Invention may be carried into practical effect it being understood that I do not necessarily limit myself to the precise materials and details of operation hereinafter given as an example, as it will be readily understood that they may be varied without departing from the nature of the said Invention.

I take melted cryolite mixed with a suitable flux or I take a mixture of other compound of aluminium and a suitable flux, the same being contained in a plumbago or wrought iron crucible or receptacle heated by any convenient arrangement of furnace, in the bottom of which crucible or receptacle is contained the metal or metals in conjunction with which the alloy of aluminium is to be made— The said metal or metals in a melted state are connected by a suitable conducting wire such as one of iron or platinum with the cathode of a powerful dynamo machine, the anode of which is connected with carbon rods placed in the melted cryolite or aluminium compound without contact with the melted metal contained in the bottom of the crucible or receptacle.

The flux constituting in effect the electrolyte must be such that it will enter very easily into combination with fluorine, liberated on the anode and it should contain as large a percentage as possible of pure aluminium— Mixtures which fulfil this condition may be obtained by melting the cryolite, or aluminium compound, with carbonate of soda or carbonate of potash, or with other carbonates, the bases of which possess a great affinity for fluorine.

The electrical current used to effect the chemical decomposition of the cryolite, or aluminium compound, must be generated by a dynamo machine giving a sufficient electromotive force to effect the chemical decomposition of the mixture, cryolite or other aluminium compound and flux, into aluminium and sodium (or its equivalent) at the negative pole, and the liberation of fluorine at the positive pole, and to overcome the resistance of the melted mixture, and also that due to the electromotive force of polarization.

When cryolite is used, I find that it is indispensable to separate the silica from the cryolite, as the silica during the process would be decomposed and the liberated silicon by entering into combination with the aluminium bronze would render it very brittle.

When a mixture of an oxide of aluminium (Al_2O_3) is employed, the flux must be used in a quantity sufficient to give an easily fusible combination— In this case the flux should consist of carbonate of potash or soda or both. By using this last method the carbon at the positive pole is not so rapidly disintegrated.

All the metals which give alloys with aluminium can be used in a melted state as the cathode for obtaining aluminium bronze according to this Invention— If the metal used be not melted (for example iron), then the aluminium can be obtained in a very thin layer covering the surface of the metal so used.

Having now described and particularly ascertained the nature of my said Invention and in what manner the same is to be performed I declare that what I claim is—

The manufacture or obtaining of aluminium Bronze by treating cryolite or other compound of aluminium and a flux, by means of a current of electricity, and in the presence of copper brass or other metals substantially as hereinbefore described.

Dated this 8th day of November 1884.

J. HENRY JOHNSON,
Agent for the said Anthony Zdziarski.

THE MOST IMPORTANT COWLES PATENT

This United States Patent Number 319,795 was applied for on December 24, 1884, and issued June 9, 1885. It covers the fusing of ore by means of internal electric heat. The concept of electrolysis was covered in the original application, but abandoned in the final wording of the patent as issued because of Patent Office claims that, with respect to electrolysis, the Cowles brothers had been anticipated by work done in Europe earlier in the century. Infringement of this patent was the basis for a suit in which the Circuit Court of Appeals in Pennsylvania in March, 1913, assessed $300,000 damages against the Carborundum Company. This patent was also the basis for an infringement suit filed by the Cowles Company in 1891 against the Pittsburgh Reduction Company which, however, had to be withdrawn because of the unexpected issue in February, 1892, of Bradley Patent Number 468,148 on which the application had been filed in 1883, thus preceding the date which could be established for the Cowles invention. The wording of this Cowles patent is as follows:

TO ALL WHOM IT MAY CONCERN:

Be it known that we, EUGENE H. COWLES and ALFRED H. COWLES, citizens of the United States, residing at Cleveland, in the county of Cuyahoga and State of Ohio, have invented certain new and useful Improvements in Processes for Smelting Ores by the Electric Current; and we do hereby declare the following to be a full, clear, and exact description of the invention, such as will enable others skilled in the art to which it appertains to make and use the same, reference being had to the accompanying drawings, and to letters or figures of reference marked thereon, which form a part of this specification.

The present invention relates to the class of smelting-furnaces which employ an electric current solely as a source of heat. Heretofore it has been attempted to reduce ores and perform metallurgical operations by means of an electric arc, the material to be treated being brought within the field of the arc or passed or fed through it; but numerous experiments have demonstrated that the arc system is not adapted for long and continuous operations on a scale of any considerable magnitude. The difficulties attending the regulation of the arc and the preservation of a constant resistance are very great, and the heat generated, though intense, is localized and difficult to control.

The object of this invention is to provide a process by which electricity can be practically employed for metallurgical operations, and for this purpose to secure a distribution of the intense heat which it is well known electricity is capable of generating over a large area or through a large mass in such a manner that a high temperature can be sustained for a long time and controlled.

To this end the invention consists, essentially, in the use for metallurgical purposes of a body of granular material of high resistance or low conductivity interposed within the circuit in such a manner as to form a continuous and unbroken part of the same, which granular body by reason of its resistance is made incandescent and generates all the heat required. The ore or light material to be reduced—as, for example, the hydrated oxide of aluminium, alum, chloride of sodium, oxide of calcium, or sulphate of strontium—is usually mixed with the body of granular resistance material, and is thus brought directly in contact with the heat at the points of generation at the same time the heat is distributed through the mass of granular material, being generated by the resistance of all the granules, and is not localized at one point or along a single line. The material best adapted for this purpose is electric-light carbon, as it possesses the necessary amount of electrical resistance, and is capable of enduring any known degree of heat when protected from oxygen without disintegrating or fusing; but crystalline silicon or other equivalent of carbon can be employed for the same purpose. This is pulverized or granulated, the degree of granulation depending upon the size of the furnace. Coarse granulated carbon works better than finely-pulverized carbon and gives more even results. The electrical energy is more evenly distributed, and the current cannot so readily form a path of highest temperature and consequently of least resistance through the mass along which the entire current or the bulk of the current can pass; but the scope of this invention is not limited by the degree of granulation, as that may vary with the conditions of the case, and with a large furnace and a powerful current the size of the carbon particles may pass beyond what is ordinarily understood by the term "granular" and be, in fact, pieces of carbon of considerable size. Still the resistance body is ordinarily composed of grains or pieces proximately equal in size, in order to secure an even distribution of the electrical energy.

The operation must necessarily be conducted within an air-tight chamber or in a non-oxidizing atmosphere, as otherwise the carbon will be consumed and act as fuel. The carbon acts as a deoxidizing agent for the ore or metalliferous material treated, and to this extent it is consumed, but otherwise than from this cause it remains unimpaired.

We will illustrate and describe a zinc-furnace embodying our invention, from which the application of the same to the reduction or smelting of other kinds of ores will be readily understood, especially of aluminium, silicium, magnesium, boron, and other rare metals, which are not reducible by the smelting processes heretofore known.

Figure 1 is a vertical longitudinal section through the center of a zinc-retort of a form similar to those used in the Belgian furnaces, and Fig. 2 is a front view of the same.

This retort consists of a cylinder, A, made of silica or other nonconducting material, suitably embedded in a body, B, of powdered charcoal, mineral wool, or of some other material which is not a good conductor of heat. The rear end of the retort-cylinder is closed by means of a carbon-plate, C, which plate forms the positive electrode, and with this plate the positive wire of the electric circuit is connected. The outer end of the retort is closed by means of an inverted graphite crucible, D, to which the negative wire of the electric circuit is attached. This graphite crucible serves as a plug for closing the end of the retort. It also forms a condensing-chamber for the zinc-fumes, and it also constitutes the negative electrode. The term "electrode" is used in this case as designating the terminals of the circuit proper, or that portion of it which acts simply as an electrical conductor, and not with the intention of indicating the ends of a line between which there is no circuit-connection. The circuit between the electrodes, so called, is continuous, being established by means of and through the body of broken carbon. The mouth of the crucible is closed with a luting of clay or otherwise, and the opening d, made in the upper side of the crucible, near its extremity, comes entirely within the retort and forms a passage for the zinc-fumes from the

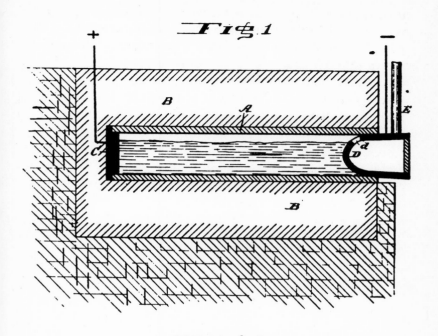

Fig. 1

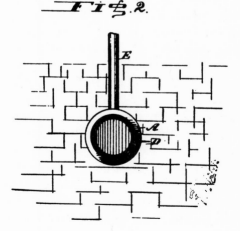

Fig. 2

retort-chamber into the condensing-chamber. The pipe E serves as a vent for the condensing-chamber. The zinc ore is mixed with the pulverized or granular carbon and the retort charged nearly full through the front end with the mixture, the plug D being removed for this purpose. A small space is left at the top, as shown. After the plug has been inserted and the joint properly luted the electric circuit is closed and the current allowed to pass through the retort, traversing its entire length through the body of mixed ore and carbon. The carbon constituents of the mass become incandescent, generating a very high degree of heat, and being in direct contact with the ore the latter is rapidly and effectually reduced and distilled.

The heat evolved distills the zinc, and the zinc-fumes are condensed in the condensing-chamber precisely as in the present method of zinc-making, with this important exception, that aside from the reaction produced by heating carbon in the presence of zinc oxide the electric current in passing through the zinc oxide has a decomposing and disintegrating action upon it, not unlike the effect produced by an electric current in a solution. This action accelerates the distillation and promotes economy in the process.

It will be observed that the intimate mixture of incandescent carbon and ore affords the most effective utilization of all the heat evolved. None of it is lost by transmission through any intervening bodies or spaces. Moreover, the maximum degree of heat generated by the furnace is within the ore body, and the retort and furnace receive only the heat which is transmitted outward from the ore and carbon contained within; consequently the retort or the furnace is not subjected to the highest degree of heat, as is the case in the Belgian method of zinc-smelting, and the life-time of a retort is thus materially increased. It is proposed to use a number of these retorts in the same circuit, in series or multiple arc, as desired.

We have found in practice that a mixture of about one part of carbon with one and a half parts of zinc ore, by weight, gives most satisfactory results with the particular ore which we have treated; but the proportions to be used will depend upon the character of the ore and the degree of heat required to reduce it, and the degree of heat evolved will be determined by the resistance or conductivity of the mass and the strength of the current employed.

Fig. 3 illustrates an improved form of furnace operating in the same manner as the one just described.

The furnace or retort chamber F has an inclined floor, sloping from both ends down to a discharge-hole, *f*, through which the metal and slag or residue can be withdrawn. G G' are the electrode-plates forming the ends of the furnace-chamber, connected, respectively, with the electric wires. H is the condenser, and I I I are hoppers for charging the furnace, several being provided, to distribute the charge evenly

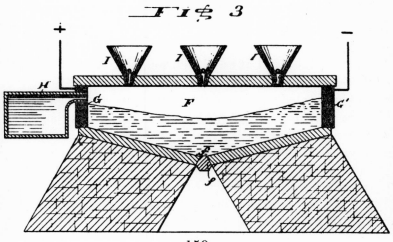

Fig. 3

along the chamber. The hoppers I and the discharge-opening f are closed with fire-clay plugs. This furnace admits of the use of heavy walls and solid permanent construction, and also a prolonged heat. A nice regulation of the resistance of the charge is secured by means of the several feed-hoppers, an additional amount being fed in when resistance is too high, and a portion of the charge being withdrawn through the bottom when the resistance is too low.

In the reduction of an ore composed of a nonvolatile metal, or a metal which is not volatilized at the heat generated in the furnace, the metal remains in the furnace mixed with the carbon filling the interstices between the grains, while the gases produced pass off. In the reduction of rare metals, where a pure product is desired, it is necessary to use a pure carbon, or a carbon free from iron or other foreign ingredient, otherwise the iron or other substance will go into the product.

We do not in this application make any claim to the furnace or apparatus herein described, as that is reserved for the subject-matter of a separate application; and we are aware that an electric current has been employed in the reduction of fused ores, and we do not claim the same, broadly; but

What we do claim as our invention, and desire to secure by Letters Patent, is—

1. The method of generating heat for metallurgical operations herein described, which consists in passing an electric current through a body of broken or pulverized resistance material that forms a continuous part of the electric circuit, the ore to be treated by the process being brought into contact with the broken or pulverized resistance material, whereby the heat is generated by the resistance of the broken or pulverized body throughout its mass, and the op-

eration can be performed solely by means of electrical energy.

2. The method of smelting or reducing ores or metalliferous compounds herein described, which consists in subjecting the ore in the presence of carbon to the action of heat generated by passing an electric current through a body of broken or pulverized resistance material that forms a continuous part of the electric circuit, the ore being in contact with the broken or pulverized resistance material, whereby the ore is reduced by the combined action of the carbon and of the heat generated solely by the resistance of the broken or pulverized body throughout its mass.

3. The method of smelting or reducing ores or metalliferous compounds herein described, which consists in pulverizing the ore and mixing with it pulverized or broken carbon or like material, then introducing the mixed ore and carbon within an electric circuit, of which it forms a continuous part, the said circuit being established through the carbon constituents of the mass, whereby the heat is generated by the electrical resistance of the carbon throughout the mass, and the operation can be performed entirely by means of the carbon reagent and the electrical energy.

4. The method of smelting or reducing ores or metalliferous compounds herein described, which consists in subjecting the ore in the presence of a reducing agent to the action of heat generated by passing an electric current through a body of broken or pulverized resistance material that forms a continuous part of the electric circuit, the ore being in contact with the broken or pulverized resistance material, whereby the ore is reduced by the combined action of the reducing agent and of the heat generated solely by the resistance of the broken or pulverized body throughout its mass.

In testimony whereof we affix our signatures in presence of two witnesses.

EUGENE H. COWLES
ALFRED H. COWLES

BRADLEY AND CROCKER PATENT

This United States Patent Number 335,499 was applied for on March 14, 1885, and issued on February 2, 1886. The application was declared by the Patent Office to be in interference with the application for Cowles Patent Number 319,795. As a result the Cowles brothers purchased this Bradley and Crocker application, and also title to other work done by Bradley in this field, Bradley and his patent attorney, Crocker, either conceding priority to the Cowles brothers or being defeated by them in interference proceedings. This patent, which covers the fusing of ore by internal electric heat, is worded as follows:

TO ALL WHOM IT MAY CONCERN:

Be it known that we, CHARLES S. BRADLEY, a citizen of the United States, residing at Yonkers, in the county of Westchester and State of New York, and FRANCIS B. CROCKER, a citizen of the United States, residing at New York, in the county and State of New York, have invented a new and useful Process of Heating and Reducing Ores by Electricity, of which the following is a specification.

In a large number of chemical and metallurgical processes in which high temperatures are required, and in which it is impossible, on account of the nature of the operation, to heat the materials by the direct action of fire in a reverberatory or blast furnace, it is customary to treat such materials in closed externally-heated crucibles or retorts. For example, the reduction of sodium, potassium, and zinc, and the manufacture of aluminium chloride, are carried on in this way; but this method is very troublesome and expensive. The crucibles or retorts are rapidly destroyed, and being necessarily small, in order that it shall not require too long to heat them through, the labor of charging and managing a large number of small retorts becomes very great.

The object of our invention is to overcome these and other difficulties, and to obtain the heat necessary to carry on such operations in a convenient and efficient manner, and to concentrate the heat exactly where it is needed; and, furthermore, our invention has for its object the attainment in commercial processes of temperatures very much higher than have ever been reached before.

Our invention is applicable to a large number of chemical and metallurgical processes; but in order to enable others to use the invention we shall describe in detail two or three of its most typical applications.

In the accompanying drawing, the figure illustrates one form of our apparatus, and represents a vertical longitudinal section of a furnace constructed according to our invention. The electrical arrangements are shown also in the figure diagrammatically.

The apparatus shown in the figure is especially designed to be employed for the reduction of sodium or potassium; and it consists of a hollow cylinder, KK, made of some suitable material which is a conductor of electricity. In this particular case it is represented as being made of wrought-iron, and is similar to the cylindrical retorts usually employed for making sodium and potassium. This cylinder K is set at a slight inclination in brick-work, as shown. On this cylinder there are two rings, L and M, of copper or other suitable metal. These rings fit the cylinder closely, so as to make good electrical connection.

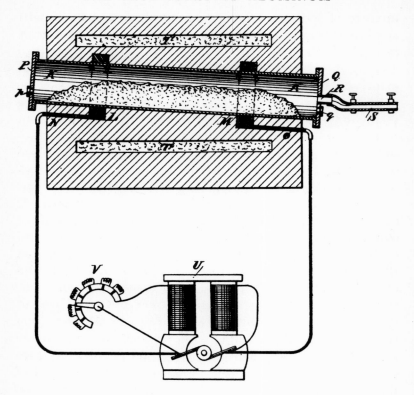

To the rings L and M are respectively connected two heavy strips of copper, N and O, which lead to the outside of the furnace. The cylinder K is provided at each end with covers or caps P and Q. In these caps there are holes p and q, closed by screw-plugs. The door Q is also fitted with a pipe, R, to the end of which a condenser, S, is attached.

In the brick-work of the furnace there are spaces TT, which may be filled with asbestus, mineral wool, or other suitable non-conductor of heat; or these spaces may be left empty, air alone being a very good insulator of heat.

In working this furnace for the production of sodium the

mixture of sodium carbonate, charcoal, and chalk usually employed in making sodium is charged into the cylinder K through the door P. The copper strips N and O are then connected, respectively, to the poles of a dynamo-electric machine, U, by large copper conductors, as indicated in the drawing, and a current of electricity is caused to pass along the cylinder K from the ring L to the ring M, the current being partly carried by the mixture contained in the cylinder, which mixture is a conductor by virtue of the carbon it contains, and partly by the metal out of which the cylinder K is made. These rings L and M distribute the current uniformly all around the cylinder. The dynamo U should be constructed to give a current of great "quantity," and the conductors and strips N and O, connecting it with the cylinder K, being made of heavy copper bars, so that the electrical resistance of the iron cylindrical shell K and of the mixture it contains will constitute the greater portion of the resistance of the circuit, consequently almost all the energy of the current will be converted into heat along the cylinder K, and since it is surrounded by non-conductors of heat the heat will accumulate and the temperature gradually rise until the heat consumed in the reduction of the sodium and lost by conduction through the walls of the furnace equals the heat produced by the passage of current.

The strength of the current, and consequently the temperature of the cylinder K, may be regulated and maintained at the proper point by means of the switch V, which governs the electro-motive force of the dynamo-machine by varying the resistance of the shunt-circuit which supplies the field-magnets, as shown.

The general method of carrying on the process is the same as in the process now commonly used for making sodium, and the sodium vapor produced by the action of the heat upon the mixture of sodium carbonate and charcoal passes out through the pipe R into the condenser S of the well-known form, P, in which it condenses and collects. The temperature and action within the cylinder may be seen by taking out the plug in either of the holes p or q. These holes also serve as poke-holes, through which the material may be poked or stirred. Fresh material is charged into the cylinder K through the door P, and any residue is taken out through the door Q. The charging of fresh material and discharging of residue is facilitated by the slope of the cylinder K, as shown in the drawing. In this way the process is made continuous and easy to manage.

Among the advantages of our process are: first, it is continuous, as we have just explained; second, the retort or cylinder is heated perfectly uniformly, instead of being heated, as sodium-retorts usually are, on the under side; third, the retort is set in solid brick-work, and is supported and held firmly in its proper place and shape on all sides; fourth, the temperature can be regulated perfectly.

In consequence of these advantages of our process the wrought-iron retorts will last almost indefinitely, whereas the retorts in the ordinary sodium process are very rapidly destroyed. In fact the renewal of retorts constitutes at present over one-half of the total cost of making sodium. This destruction of retorts is caused by the uneven heating, the strain due to their own weight and that of the materials they contain, and the "scaling" action of the hot gases, all of which difficulties, as we have already shown, are avoided in our process.

In actual practice our apparatus may be constructed and arranged as follows: We generally prefer to have a number of furnaces or apparatuses like the one shown in Fig. 1, and connect them so that the current will flow through them in series. For this purpose a dynamo must of course be used of correspondingly higher electro-motive force.

Potassium may be reduced by our process in precisely the same manner as we have described for sodium, except that a little higher temperature is required.

In employing our process for making zinc we use the same mixture of roasted zinc ore (zinc oxide) and carbon that is ordinarily used; but the cylinder A should be made of carbon instead of iron. The material consisting of graphite and clay, out of which the common graphite crucibles are made, is well adapted to the purpose. Otherwise the apparatus and process are substantially the same as the sodium process already described.

Instead of using a cylinder made in one place, a chamber may be built up of a number of pieces. For example, the retort K in the figure may be made of plates of iron, and in the case of the furnace for reducing zinc a chamber may be built of bricks composed of the material referred to above out of which graphite crucibles are made.

The manufacture of aluminium chloride may be carried on by our process in an apparatus similar to that shown in Fig. 1; but in this case the cylinder K should be placed vertically, as in the ordinary form of apparatus used for making this chloride. The cylinder should in this case be made of graphite and clay, as in the zinc process already described, and the cylinder is heated by passing an electric current through it, as in the figure. The well-known mixture of alumina and carbon made up into balls is charged into the retort, and a stream of chlorine gas is introduced at the bottom of the cylinder, and the action of this upon the heated mixture of alumina and carbon produces aluminium chloride, which distills over through a pipe leading out of the upper part of the cylinder, and is collected in a suitable vessel or chamber.

It is obvious that other chemical and metallurgical processes may be carried on according to our invention in substantially the same manner as those we have described. It is also evident that various forms of furnace and built of various materials may be employed without departing from our invention. For example, in the form of furnace shown in the figure, instead of entirely surrounding the materials with an electrical conducting-cylinder, through which a current is passed, a conductor may be placed in the bottom alone and the materials laid upon it; or conductors may be placed in the sides or in the top of the chamber, in which latter case the materials would be heated by radiation from the heated conductors above them, which in some cases is a very desirable arrangement.

In an application for Letters Patent of the United States now pending (filed February 23, 1883, Serial No. 85,957) Charles S. Bradley, one of the present inventors, has described an electro-metallurgical process in which an electric current is employed to perform two functions: first, to effect the electrolytic decomposition of the materials treated, and, second, to supply the heat necessary to maintain said materials in the fused state while they are being electrolyzed.

The present invention resembles the above to a certain extent; but in the present invention the electric current which we employ performs no electrolytic action, the reaction which takes place being purely chemical, and the function of the current being solely to develop the heat which is a necessary condition of the reaction. For this reason our invention does not require the use of a continuous current of electricity. An alternating current may be employed, if desired, which is an advantage, since large alternating-current dynamos may be constructed more cheaply than the continuous-current machines, and it is also less trouble and expense to run them.

We are aware that in English Patents No. 4,043 of 1878

and No. 2,110 of 1879 processes are described in which materials are heated by means of electric currents. In one of these patents the heat of the electric arc is employed to fuse metals. In the other patent a furnace is described to be used for metallurgical processes, cooking meats, &c., in which the heat is produced by passing an electric current around the sides of the furnace; but no mention is made of mixing the materials with carbon and passing an electric current through the mixture.

In United States Patent No. 282,964, dated August 14, 1883, Delaplaine *et al.* describe a process for melting the tin off of common scrap sheet-tin by placing the scrap in a closed furnace and passing an electric current through it; but in this process there is no chemical action, and no carbon is mixed with the material.

We do not claim as our invention the arrangement of the material to be subjected to be treated in the form of a shallow deposit, or a furnace adapted to receive such a charge in the form of a shallow deposit; and we also disclaim the arrangement of oppositely-located carbon plates for conducting the current to the charge as being our invention.

Having now described our invention, what we claim, and desire to secure by Letters Patent, is—

1. The electrical heating process hereinbefore described, which consists in passing an electric current along the walls of a retort, which are composed of a conducting material, and are in superficial contact with a mixture of conducting material and material to be heated, which mixture is thereby included in the circuit, so that the walls of the retort and the mixture will constitute the greater portion of the resistance of the circuit, substantially as and for the purpose set forth.

2. The electrical heating process hereinbefore described, which consists in placing a mixture of charcoal and the material to be heated in a cylindrical iron retort surrounded by material which is a bad conductor of heat, and passing an electric current through the walls of the retort, so that the mixture in contact with them is included in the circuit, and so that the walls of the retort and the mixture will constitute the greater portion of the resistance of the circuit, substantially as and for the purpose set forth.

CHARLES S. BRADLEY
FRANCIS B. CROCKER

COWLES-MABERY PATENT COVERING PRODUCTION OF ALUMINUM

This United States Patent Number 324,659 was issued to the Cowles brothers and Professor Charles F. Mabery of Cleveland on August 18, 1885, having been applied for April 23, 1885, as a division of the original Cowles application of December 24, 1884. It covers two alternative ways of producing pure aluminum, the first step in each case being the production of an alloy through fusing ore in the electric furnace. Neither of these methods was sufficiently economical to compete with the alumina-cryolite process of Hall and Héroult which was developed the following year. The Cowles-Mabery patent was as follows:

TO ALL WHOM IT MAY CONCERN:

Be it known that we, EUGENE H. COWLES, ALFRED H. COWLES, and CHARLES F. MABERY, citizens of the United States, residing at Cleveland, in the county of Cuyahoga and State of Ohio, have invented a certain new and useful Improvement in Process of Electric Smelting for Obtaining Aluminium; and we do hereby declare the following to be a full, clear, and exact description of the invention, such as will enable others skilled in the art to which it appertains to make and use the same.

This invention relates to the reduction of aluminous ores and the production of aluminium by electricity.

Heretofore many processes have been proposed by others for the reduction of aluminium, but they have been too expensive to allow the metal to be produced at a price low enough for it to come into extensive and general use, and in prior patents, Nos. 319,945 and 319,795, of June 9, 1885, by two of the undersigned, an electric furnace and process of reducing ores have been described, by means of which aluminium, as well as other refractory ores, can be economically reduced. Ores are reduced in said furnace by mixing them with broken or granular carbon and passing an electric current through a charge of the mixed ore and carbon; but the product thereby obtained, when an ore of aluminium is reduced, contains a considerable percentage of carbon, which is taken up both chemically and mechanically by the aluminium; and the object of the present invention is to provide a process whereby the aluminium can be obtained free from carbon and in a pure metallic state. This we accomplish by reducing the ore of aluminium in company with tin, copper, manganese, or other metal which will alloy with the aluminium, and then subsequently separating the alloying metal from the aluminium by amalgamation, lixiviation, or equivalent process, leaving the residue aluminium in the form of an amorphous powder or state, which can be melted down into an ingot. When aluminium is alloyed with either of the metals above named it takes up very little, if any, of the carbon, whereas the pure aluminium will, as above stated, absorb a very considerable percentage of carbon, more even than iron or any of the other metals. We thus obtain an alloy free from carbon, and the constituent elements of the alloy may be separated in several ways—for example, in some cases by amalgamation and in others by lixiviation.

To produce aluminium according to this process, a charge of the pulverized ore of aluminium and carbon mixed is reduced by means of an electric current in company with the alloying metal, and this step in the process is fully described in an application filed by E. H. Cowles and A. H. Cowles on the 7th of April, 1885. The product thereby obtained is an alloy of aluminium with tin, manganese, or such other metal as may be preferred, but either tin or manganese are preferably used, and the alloy is substantially free from carbon chemically combined therewith. The alloy as it comes from the furnace has pieces of the carbon attached to and embedded in it, and the carbon thus mechanically united with the alloy is easily removed by crushing the mass and washing.

When the aluminium is alloyed with tin, silver, copper, or other easily-amalgamated metal, the two metals are easily separated by amalgamation in the same manner that gold or silver ores are amalgamated. The mercury takes up the alloying metal and leaves the aluminium untouched, and the amalgamation may be effected either with or without the use of sodium amalgam, acid, electricity, or heat to assist and quicken the amalgamation. If manganese or some other readily soluble metal—as zinc or copper—is used, then any lixiviation process may be employed that will leach out the alloying metal.

The alloy may be broken into small pieces and placed in a suitable vessel, through which a lixiviating liquid—such as nitric acid and water—is caused to flow and leach out the manganese from the alloy, the aluminium not being touched by the lixiviation process; and the said lixiviation may be assisted by other acids, heat, or electricity, as the case may require. In both cases the residue is aluminium in the form of an amorphous powder, and this is easily melted into an ingot.

We do not confine the use of the hereinbefore-described process to the production of aluminium, as the same method may be followed to obtain other like metals, and also met-alloids—such as silicium and boron.

We are aware that it has been heretofore proposed to re-duce aluminium ores by smelting them with zinc ores and then separating the two metals, and that the alkaline earths have been reduced by electrolysis in contact with an alloy-ing metal and plates of carbon or platinum, and the alloyed metals thus produced subsequently separated. We do not, therefore, claim the same, broadly; but

What we do claim as our invention, and desire to secure by Letters Patent, is—

1. The method of producing aluminium which consists in reducing an ore or compound of aluminium in company with an amalgamating metal by means of electricity and in the presence of carbon, substantially as described, and then separating the two metals of the alloy by amalgamation.

2. The method of producing aluminium which consists of mixing the aluminium ore with carbon and with a metal, reducing the said ore by means of electricity, so that the alu-minium forms an alloy with the said metal, and finally sepa-rating the two metals of the alloy, substantially as set forth.

3. The method of producing aluminium which consists of mixing the aluminium ore with broken carbon and with a metal, reducing the said ore by means of electricity, so that the aluminium forms an alloy with the metal, and finally

separating the aluminium from the alloy by amalgamating the said metal, substantially as set forth.

In testimony whereof we affix our signatures in presence of two witnesses.

EUGENE H. COWLES
CHARLES F. MABERY
ALFRED H. COWLES

MOST IMPORTANT HÉROULT PATENT

French Patent Number 175,711 was issued to Paul L. T. Héroult on April 23, 1886. It covers the production of pure aluminum by electrolysis of alumina dissolved in cryolite fused by external heat. The process is essentially the same as that developed simultaneously by Charles Martin Hall in the United States. The following is an English translation of Héroult's French patent:

In principle the process for the preparation of aluminum which I wish to patent consists in decomposing alumina dissolved in a fused bath of cryolite, by an electric current which traverses the bath, on the one part by means of an electrode in contact with the crucible of compressed carbon which contains the cryolite, and on the other part by means of another electrode, of hard carbon like the first, which dips into the bath. That combination produces the decomposition of alumina by employing a current of feeble tension. The oxygen is set free at the anode and burns with it, the aluminum deposits on the walls of the crucible which constitutes the cathode and precipitates in a button in the bottom of the crucible.

The bath remains constant and may be used indefinitely if it is fed with alumina.

The positive electrode, that is to say, the anode, is to be replaced after combustion, but that combustion prevents polarization, and by that fact ensures constancy in the energy and action of the electric current.

For explanation only, I add to this description a drawing which represents, in vertical section, an installation based upon the principle above described.

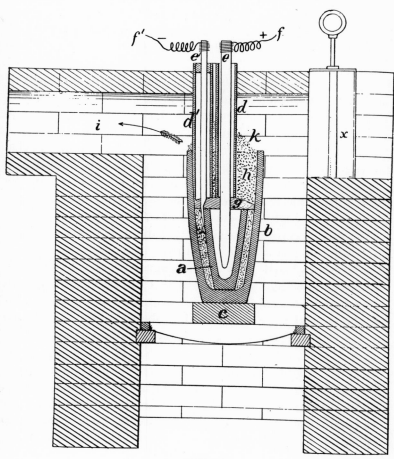

The crucible a which contains the bath of cryolite (natural fluoride of aluminum and sodium) is of hard carbon very dense and conductive. It is placed in another crucible b of plumbago, set upon a thick disc or other support c interposed between it and the grate of the furnace.

The electrodes e e^1 are sticks of hard carbon. The anode e is arranged in the axis of the crucible a in such manner as to dip into the bath, while the cathode e^1 makes contact with the crucible itself. The electrodes extend to just above the arch of the furnace, and stoneware tubes d d^1 protect them from the contact of the air and from the action of the fire.

To the positive electrode e is attached the conductor f and to the negative electrode e^1 the conductor f^1, which conductors come from a dynamo-electric machine of suitable power and of low tension.

The crucible a is closed by a cover g of magnesia or clay through which the anode e passes. Above this I arrange a layer of films of refractory clay h, which is covered finally by a cap of loose earth or fireclay k. The chimney of the furnace is at i and the entrance at x.

When the cryolite is melted the bath is electrolyzed by carrying the electric current through the electrodes e e^1. There is produced then a disengagement of oxygen upon the anode e, which, being at a high temperature, burns with it with the formation of oxide of carbon which passes out by the central tube d, the other tube d^1 being kept closed to prevent the access of air. Upon the other side the aluminum is set free at the cathode, that is to say, upon the interior walls of the crucible a, where it deposits and falls into the bottom of the crucible, and finally forms a button.

The cryolite always remains. It suffices in order to render the production of metal continuous to add anew alumina to replace that which has been previously decomposed.

I estimate that a current of one to two volts is sufficient for the commercial success of the process, which is an important economy compared with all the attempts hitherto made, which have always required currents of an energy at least twice as great. The reason for this is that in my process the carbon of the positive electrode e in burning evolves a quantity of heat which does not need to be furnished by the electric current. The anode is consumed in each of the operations; for three equivalents of carbon burned we obtain two equivalents of aluminum.

The same method is equally applicable to the treatment of the borate and of the silicate of alumina, always by adding alumina *in excess* to re-establish the initial composition of the bath of cryolite.

To Sum Up: I claim the invention of the above described process for the preparation of aluminum, which consists of electrolyzing alumina in solution in fused cryolite, which receives the electrodes in any convenient manner; for example, the anode dipping into the cryolite while the cathode makes contact with the hard carbon crucible which contains the bath, from which it results that oxygen evolves upon the anode and burns with it and that the aluminum separates at the cathode as fast as the electrolyzation takes place, and deposits in a button at the bottom of the crucible.

I claim as an integral part of my invention the application of the same process to the treatment of the borate and of the silicate of alumina, always adding, as I have said, alumina in excess in order to re-establish the initial composition of the bath of cryolite.

I remark, finally, that the arrangement first above described and represented in the annexed drawing, is only given for the understanding of my new process, but that

I expressly intend to reserve to myself the privilege of employing any other arrangement more or less industrial.

Paris, April 23, 1886.

For representation of Mr. P. L. T. Héroult.

Signed: BLETRY BROTHERS.

MOST IMPORTANT HALL PATENT

This United States Patent Number 400,766 was issued to Charles Martin Hall on April 2, 1889, having been applied for on July 9, 1886. It covers the production of pure aluminum by electrolysis of alumina dissolved in cryolite which has been fused by external heat. This is essentially the same process as the one developed at that time in France by Paul L. T. Héroult. The following is Hall's patent:

TO ALL WHOM IT MAY CONCERN:

Be it known that I, CHARLES M. HALL, a citizen of the United States, residing at Oberlin, in the county of Lorain and State of Ohio, have invented certain new and useful Improvements in the Process of Reducing Aluminium by Electrolysis; and I do hereby declare the following to be a full, clear, and exact description of the invention, such as will enable others skilled in the art to which it appertains to make and use the same.

The invention described herein relates to the reduction of aluminium from its oxide by dissolving such oxide in a bath containing a fused fluoride salt of aluminium and then reducing the aluminium by passing an electric current through the bath; and in general terms the invention consists in the electrolysis of a solution of alumina in a fused fluoride salt of aluminium, substantially as hereinafter more fully described and claimed.

178

In the accompanying drawings, forming a part of this specification, Figure 1 is a sectional elevation of a form of apparatus applicable in the practice of my invention; and Fig. 2 is a view, partly in elevation and partly in section, of a modified form of apparatus.

In the practice of my invention I prepare a bath for the solution of the alumina by fusing together in a suitable crucible, A, the fluoride of aluminium and the fluoride of a metal more electro-positive than aluminium—as, for example, the fluoride of sodium potassium, &c.—these salts being preferably mingled together in the proportions of eighty-four parts of sodium fluoride and one hundred and sixty-nine parts of aluminium fluoride, represented by the formula $Na_2Al_2F_8$. A convenient method of forming the bath consists in adding to the mineral cryolite 338/421 of its weight of aluminium fluoride. The object of thus adding aluminium fluoride is to secure in the bath the proper relative proportions of the fluorides of aluminium and sodium. To this fused bath is added alumina or the oxide of aluminium in sufficient quantities, and the alumina being dissolved by the fused bath an electric current is passed through the solution, by means of suitable electrodes, C and D, connected with a dynamo-electric machine or other suitable source of electricity and immersed in the solution. By the action of the electric current, which preferably has an electro-motive force of about four to six volts, oxygen is released at the positive electrode C, and aluminium is reduced at the negative electrode D, which, on account of the affinity of aluminium for other metals, is formed of carbon when it is desired to produce pure aluminium. The positive electrode may be formed of carbon, copper, platinum, or other suitable material. When formed of carbon, the electrode C is gradually consumed, and must therefore be renewed from time to time; but when formed of copper an

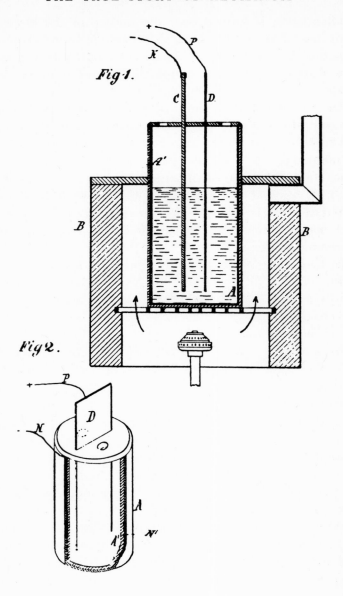

Fig 1.

Fig 2.

oxide coating is formed over the surface of the electrode. This coating serves to protect the electrode from further destruction by the action of the oxygen, but does not interfere materially with the conducting qualities of the electrode.

On account of the affinity of aluminium for other metals, and also the corrosive action of the materials forming the bath on earthy materials, I prefer to form the crucible or melting-pot A of metal—as iron or steel—and protect the same from the action of the aluminium by a carbon lining, A'. This crucible is placed in a suitable furnace, B, and subjected to a sufficient heat to fuse the materials placed therein, such materials fusing at approximately the same temperature as common salt.

In lieu of the electrode D, as shown in Fig. 1, the carbon lining A' may be employed as the negative electrode, as shown in Fig. 2, the conductor from the negative pole of the electric generator being suitably connected, as shown at N', to such lining.

In order to render the bath or solvent more fusible fluoride of lithium may be substituted for a portion of the fluoride of sodium—as, for example, for one-fourth of the fluoride of sodium an equivalent amount of lithium fluoride by molecular weights may be substituted. Thus twenty-six parts of lithium fluoride displacing forty-two parts of sodium fluoride, the resulting combination contains twenty-six parts of lithium fluoride for every one hundred and twenty-six parts of sodium fluoride and three hundred and thirty-eight parts of aluminium fluoride.

While I consider the proportions of fluorides of sodium and aluminium, and of the fluorides of sodium, lithium, and aluminium, hereinbefore stated, as best adapted for the purpose, such proportions may be varied within certain limits without materially affecting the operation or function of the bath, as, in fact, any proportions which may be found suitable may be employed. The aluminium as it is reduced at the negative electrode is melted and collects thereon in globules, and then drops down to the bottom of the bath, which is of less specific gravity than the molten aluminium, and can be removed by suitable means; or the bath may be poured out and after being cooled the aluminium may be picked out.

As hereinbefore stated, the oxygen is released at the positive electrode, and when the latter is formed of carbon combines therewith, forming carbonic oxide, (CO,) the carbon being gradually consumed, and with some salts, more particularly the salts of sodium, carbonaceous material is preferably used in the positive electrode or anode; but when the positive electrode is formed of copper, as is preferable when salts of potassium are employed, a copper-oxide coating is first formed on the electrode, thereby forming a protective covering, free oxygen being subsequently given off at the positive electrode.

No claim is made herein specifically to the use of the fluoride of potassium and aluminium as a bath for the reduction of aluminium, as the same forms the subject-matter of an application filed February 2, 1887, and numbered Serially 226,206; nor does the apparatus described herein with more or less particularity form any part of the invention herein, as the same forms the subject-matter of an application, No. 282,952, filed August 17, 1888.

I claim herein as my invention—

1. As an improvement in the art of manufacturing aluminium, the herein-described process, which consists in dissolving alumina in a fused bath composed of the fluorides of aluminium and a metal more electro-positive than alu-

minium, and then passing an electric current through the fused mass, substantially as set forth.

2. As an improvement in the art of manufacturing aluminium, the herein-described process, which consists in dissolving alumina in a fused bath composed of the fluorides of aluminium and sodium, and then passing an electric current, by means of a carbonaceous anode, through the fused mass, substantially as set forth.

3. As an improvement in the art of manufacturing aluminium, the herein-described process, which consists in dissolving alumina in a fused bath composed of the fluorides of aluminium, sodium, and lithium, and then passing an electric current, by means of a carbonaceous anode, through the fused mass, substantially as set forth.

In testimony whereof I affix my signature in presence of two witnesses.

CHARLES M. HALL

HALL'S PATENT COVERING PROCESS
HE WAS ADVOCATING AT LOCKPORT IN 1887-1888

This United States Patent Number 400,664 was issued to Charles Martin Hall on April 2, 1889, having been applied for February 2, 1887, as a division of his original application filed July 9, 1886. It includes the employment of external combustion heat to fuse a bath composed mainly of the double fluoride of aluminum and potassium. Copper anodes are employed for electrolysis of the dissolved alumina. This represents the process which Hall was attempting unsuccessfully to employ at the Cowles plant in Lockport, New York, during the 12 months following July, 1887. The following is the specification of this patent:

To all whom it may concern:

Be it known that I, CHARLES M. HALL, a citizen of the United States, residing at Oberlin, in the county of Lorain and State of Ohio, have invented certain new and useful Improvements in the Process of Reducing Aluminium from its Fluoride Salts by Electrolysis; and I do hereby declare the following to be a full, clear, and exact description of the invention, such as will enable others skilled in the art to which it appertains to make and use the same.

In an application, Serial No. 207,601, filed by me July 9, 1886, I have described and claimed a process for reducing aluminium, consisting in dissolving alumina or the oxide of aluminium in a fused bath composed of the fluorides of aluminium, and a metal more electro-positive than aluminium, and then passing an electric current through the fused mass, and in said application the combination of the fluorides of aluminium and sodium for the formation of the bath was claimed as a species or instance under the generic combination.

The invention described herein consists in the formation of a bath or solvent for the alumina by combining in suitable proportions the fluorides of aluminium and potassium, substantially as hereinafter more fully described and claimed.

In the accompanying drawings, forming a part of this specification, Figure 1 is a sectional elevation of a form of apparatus applicable in carrying out my invention; and Figs. 2 and 3 are views, partly in section, of modified forms of crucible.

In the practice of my invention I form a fused bath or solvent for the alumina by melting in a crucible, A, a combination of the salts known as the "fluoride of aluminium" and the "fluoride of potassium." This combination, which may also be termed the "double fluoride of aluminium and

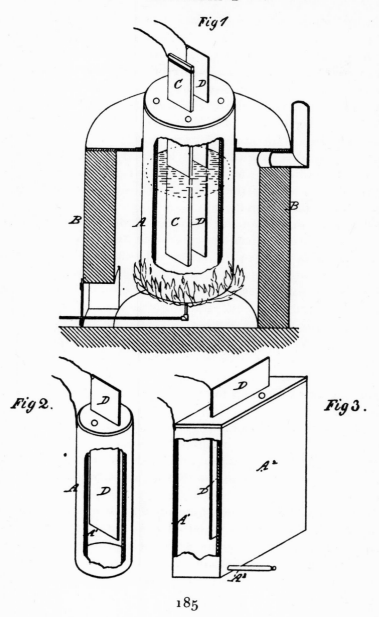

Fig 1

Fig 2.

Fig 3.

potassium," is preferably formed by mixing together one hundred and sixty-nine parts of aluminium fluoride and one hundred and sixteen parts of potassium fluoride, such proportions of the ingredients corresponding to the formula $K_2Al_2F_8$. A variation in these proportions with certain limits produces only immaterial changes in operativeness of my process—as, for example, (as I now believe the fact to be,) a larger proportion of potassium fluoride increases the capacity of the bath for dissolving alumina at the same time lessens its fusibility, whereas a larger proportion of aluminium fluoride renders the bath more fusible, but decreases its capacity for dissolving alumina.

The combination of the fluorides of aluminium and potassium may be rendered more fusible and its capacity for dissolving alumina may be increased by the addition of lithium fluoride, or a partial substitution thereof, for potassium fluoride—as, for example, the combinations of the fluorides of aluminium, potassium, and lithium, represented by the formulas $KLiAl_2F_8$ or $K_3Li_3Al_4F_{18}$, are effective as regards their capability for dissolving alumina, and are quite fusible. These compounds or combinations of the fluorides of aluminium, potassium, and lithium can be conveniently made by saturating and neutralizing with hydrofluoric acid suitable proportions of hydrate of alumina and carbonate of potassium or lithium.

The crucible A, containing the above-described bath or solvent, is placed in a suitable furnace, B, and heated sufficiently to melt the bath—*i.e.*, to approximately a low red heat. The electrodes C and D, having suitable connections with a dynamo-electric machine or other suitable source of electric energy, are then inserted into the bath and a sufficient amount of alumina placed therein. The alumina is dissolved by the bath, and by the action of the electric current aluminium is reduced at the negative electrode D, and, being melted, sinks down to the bottom of the crucible. In making pure aluminium the negative electrode D should be formed of carbon or metal coated with carbon, so as to protect the metal from the aluminium, which has a great affinity for other metals. The oxygen goes to the positive electrode C, which may be formed of copper, platinum, or other suitable non-carbonaceous material. When the positive electrode is formed of copper, it soon becomes coated with an oxide of copper, which, while not materially affecting its conducting qualities under these conditions, forms a protecting covering over the surface of the copper as against the action of the oxygen, such oxygen thereafter escaping in a free state at the positive electrode. The aluminium may be removed from the crucible as it accumulates by any suitable means, or the contents of the crucible may be poured out and cooled, and the aluminium then separated from the solvent.

On account of the affinity which aluminium has for other metals, and also the corrosive action of fluorides on earthy materials, I prefer to form the crucible of metal—as iron, steel, copper, &c.—and protect the same from the action of aluminium by a carbon lining, A', as shown. The carbon lining A' may be employed as the negative electrode, as shown in Figs. 2 and 3, and as it is desirable that the negative electrode should have a large exposed surface, I prefer an arrangement of apparatus wherein the carbon lining is so employed.

Although a higher temperature may be employed, a low red heat is sufficient for carrying on the process, and on account of the liability of reducing the solvent I prefer to employ an electric current of low electro-motive force—as, for example, three or four volts, more or less.

As shown in Fig. 3, the crucible may be provided at its

lower end with a discharge-tube, A³, through which the aluminium may be drawn off from the crucible from time to time, as desired, without interrupting the reducing operation.

I claim herein as my invention—

1. As an improvement in the art of manufacturing aluminium, the herein-described process, which consists in dissolving alumina in a fused bath composed of the fluorides of aluminium and potassium, and then passing an electric current, by means of an anode formed of non-carbonaceous material, through the fused mass, substantially as set forth.

2. As an improvement in the art of manufacturing aluminium, the herein-described process, which consists in dissolving alumina in a fused bath composed of the fluorides of aluminium, potassium, and lithium, and then passing an electric current through the fused mass, substantially as set forth.

In testimony whereof I affix my signature in presence of two witnesses.

CHARLES M. HALL

HÉROULT'S PATENT COVERING PRODUCTION OF ALUMINUM BRONZE

After Héroult had developed his process for the manufacture of pure aluminum, he was told that there was more demand for aluminum bronze. He thereupon invented a process for producing this alloy on which French Patent Number 170,003 was issued to him under date of April 15, 1887.

The following is an English translation of this French patent:

When my process is followed for the manufacture of the aluminum bronze, it consists of an electrolysis of the melted alumina in presence of the copper.

One operates then as indicated in the drawing, placing the crucible d' on a conductor carbon plate p which leads to

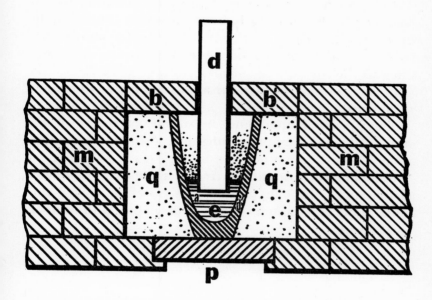

the crucible the negative pole of the current and plunging into the center of the said crucible a positive carbon d, mobile in the vertical sense by a screw or otherwise.

The crucible is surrounded by powdered gas-carbon q which shields it from the contact with the air and prevents the cooling.

b,b', bricks serving as cover for the crucible and as guide to the vertical carbon d.

m, brick chamber in which are installed the crucible and its sheathing of powdered gas-carbon.

The melted copper is at *e*; the melted alumina is at *a* and the unmelted alumina at *a'*, this latter constituting a cover which opposes the cooling.

If an electric current of great intensity is made to pass, the aluminum produced is carried on the copper.

The operation lasts as long as alumina is added and the metal obtained does not become lighter than the melted alumina.

The electric current produces enough heat to keep the alumina melted.

In an analogous manner, the alloy of iron and aluminum is obtained.

The alloying of aluminum and silicon operates when, instead of decomposing pure aluminum, a silicate of alumina is decomposed.

In summary, this addition includes the above specified modifications to obtain, by an electrolysis of the melted alumina, alloys of aluminum, either with copper, with iron, or with silicon.

HÉROULT'S BRITISH PATENT

Héroult's agent, Arthur Charles Henderson, filed for him on March 21, 1888, the complete amended specification for his British Patent Number 7426. This describes the production of pure aluminum by electrolysis of alumina dissolved in cryolite fused by internal electric heat, whereas his French Patent Number 175,711 of April 23, 1886, contemplated the use of external heat to fuse the cryolite. Acquisition in 1894 of Héroult's British Patent gave the British Aluminium Company a monopoly of aluminum production in the British Empire. The following is its complete specification:

I, Arthur Charles Henderson, of 46, Southampton Buildings, Holborn, in the County of Middlesex, and of 31, Lincoln Place, Leinster Street, Dublin, Patent Agent, do hereby declare the nature of this invention (which has been communicated to me from abroad by Paul Louis Toussaint Heroult, Metallurgist, of the City of Paris, in the Republic of France) and in what manner the same is to be performed to be particularly described and ascertained in and by the following statement:—

According to this invention aluminium is produced from alumina by electrolysis as I will hereinafter describe, cryolite being used as a flux in fusing the alumina to be electrolysed.

In connection with a crucible of agglomerated carbon a positive electrode or anode is provided the crucible itself forming a negative electrode or cathode; cryolite in the crucible forms a bath into which dips the positive electrode which is of carbon.

With this combination alumina being placed in the crucible and a current of low tension being employed the alumina is decomposed; the oxygen passes to the positive electrode or anode with which it is burnt while aluminium settles upon the walls of the crucible forming the negative electrode or cathode and settles on the bottom of the same in a metallic form or mass.

The bath of cryolite remains constant and may be used in a continuous manner alumina being fed in as required; combustion will take place of the positive electrode or anode whereby polarization will be prevented, and a constant energy and uniform action of the electric current will result, care being taken to renew the said electrode from time to time as required. The combustion of the positive electrode by the oxygen disengaged from the reduced oxide diminishes the quantity of electrical energy required to heat the bath and causes the production of an electric current in the same direction as the principal electrolysing current thereby further economizing electrical energy.

For the purpose of enabling this part of the invention to be clearly understood reference is had to Fig. 1 of the drawings filed with my Provisional Specification, which it is to be understood is intended merely as explanatory of the invention and represents a vertical section of an apparatus adapted for the production of aluminium according to my invention.

a is a crucible containing the bath of cryolite (natural fluoride of aluminium and sodium); it is formed of very dense and well conducting agglomerated carbon. It is placed within another crucible b made of graphite or plumbago and resting upon a circular or other base plate or support c of any suitable material interposed between it and the furnace grate. e e^1 are pencil shaped agglomerated carbon rods of which e serves as the positive electrode or anode. This positive electrode is arranged centrally within the crucible a and dips into the bath. The carbon rod e^1 is in direct contact with the crucible which serves as the negative electrode or cathode. The carbon rods e e^1 which are insulated from each other rise above the arch of the furnace and are protected from the action of air and fire by stoneware tubes d d^1.

A conductor f is connected to the positive electrode or anode e and a conductor f^1 is attached to the carbon e^1; these conductors f f^1 are connected with an electric generator of suitable power and low tension.

The crucible a is closed by a lid g made of refractory material such as calcined magnesia or of clay, and through which the positive electrode or anode e passes.

Over this cover is placed a layer of grout of fire clay h

FIG _ I _

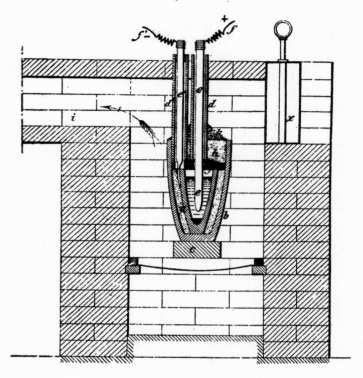

FIG _ 2 _

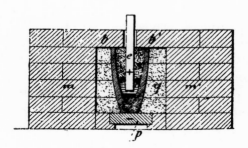

which is finally covered with a mass k of suitable material such as vegetable mould or loam.

i is the flue and x the charging door of the furnace by which the crucibles a and b are heated.

When the cryolite to which alumina has been previously added, is in a molten state, an electric current is sent through it and the alumina electrolysed.

The oxygen evolved from the alumina unites with the positive electrode or anode e, which being brought to a high temperature combines with the oxygen and forms oxide of carbon which escapes through the tube d. The tube d^1 is kept closed to prevent the entrance of air. The aluminium reduced from the alumina passes to the cathode, that is to say, to the internal walls of the crucible a, where it first settles and then falls to the bottom of the crucible where it finally forms a metallic mass.

The cryolite remains unchanged. To render the production of metal continuous alumina must be added from time to time as required to replace that previously decomposed.

For the successful and practical carrying out of this part of the invention a current of three volts has been found sufficient; this results in a considerable saving of electrical energy as compared with the processes at present in use and which invariably require currents of at least ten times greater tension. The reason for this is that in my improved process the carbon of the positive electrode e while it burns, yields an amount of heat which is not necessary to be supplied by the electric current. For three equivalents of positive carbon electrode consumed two equivalents of aluminium are obtained.

For the purpose of enabling the operator to know the condition of matters with respect to the distance apart of the electrodes an ampere meter is inserted in the circuit and by watching it the operator can tell whether the proper distance between the electrodes is being maintained, as if not the needle of the meter will be affected.

If the needle has slight oscillations or deflections alumina must be added, and the positive electrode must be slightly raised until such indications cease to be given by the meter.

For the treatment of alumina by electrolysis on a commercial scale, according to this invention, it will usually be more advantageous to use apparatus such as described in the Specification of an application for Letters Patent No. 16853, dated 7th December 1887, by William Lloyd Wise, for an invention of "Improvements in Apparatus for Producing Aluminium and other Metals and their Alloys and operating the same" communicated to him from abroad by The Schweizerische Metallurgische Gesellschaft; but it is to be noted that the said invention is not claimed herein as forming any part of the invention, the subject matter of the application for Letters Patent to which the present specification relates.

Having now particularly described the nature of this invention and in what manner the same is to be performed, I hereby declare that I am aware metal has been melted in vessels by electricity without the application of external heat, the metal so melted serving as one pole of the electric circuit; also that cryolite has been melted and electrolytically decomposed for the production of aluminium by the passage of an electric current therethrough and between positive and negative carbon electrodes without the application of external heat; also that it has been proposed to produce alloys of aluminium by the electrolytical decomposition of an aluminium compound rendered fusible by the use of a flux, the said aluminium compound and flux and also the metal intended to be alloyed with the reduced aluminium being intended to be melted by the application of external heat to the vessel containing them. I am likewise aware that it has been proposed to employ carbon lined crucibles in the production of aluminium. And I desire to have it noted that I do not claim broadly the melting and electrolytical decomposition of metallic compounds by the aid of electricity without the application of external heat for the production of metallic alloys or compounds, neither do I claim broadly the use of a molten metal negative electrode formed of one of the alloying metals or the use of a carbon lined crucible, but what I do claim is:—

1. The production of aluminium from alumina by the hereinbefore described electrolytic process using cryolite as a flux in fusing the alumina to be electrolysed.

Dated this 21st day of March 1888.

A. C. HENDERSON

Appendix C

The World's First Electric Furnace

The following is a paper presented by Eugene H. Cowles at a meeting of the Franklin Institute in Philadelphia on January 20, 1886, and published in the February, 1886, number of the Institute's Journal. This describes an electric furnace developed by Eugene H. and Alfred H. Cowles of Cleveland, which was the first in the world to be used experimentally and commercially for the reduction of ore.

MR. PRESIDENT, AND MEMBERS OF THE INSTITUTE:

In order that I may give you as brief and explicit an explanation as possible of our discovery, process and inventions, I will first proceed with a description of the plant of the Cowles Electric Smelting and Aluminum Company, now in operation at the works of the Brush Electric Company, at Cleveland, O.:

The apparatus used by us for the purpose of experiment in the reduction of refractory ores for the production of metallic calcium, magnesium, potassium, sodium, silicon, titanium, and the manufacture of aluminum and aluminum-bronze and other alloys, consists of two large Brush dynamos, two resistance boxes and two ammeters, a drying pan, eight fire-brick furnaces, suitable electrical conductors and switches, hoods for carrying off vapor and gases, large carbons—3 x 30 inches—for electrodes, screens for sizing charcoal and carbon, and a large mortar and pestle and several washing vats for washing and concentrating the furnace products. Steam-power to drive the dynamos is furnished by the "Brush Electric Company." The arrangement of the plant so as to effect the reduction of the above-named metals and metaloids, by means of carbon as the sole re-agent, is as follows:

The Dynamos.—These are, of course, placed in the dynamo room as near as possible to the driving shaft, where they can be kept free from any dust or grit from the furnace room. The larger of these is by far the most powerful machine ever built by the "Brush Electric Company." It weighs over 7,000 pounds, and at a speed of 907 revolutions per minute produces a current of 1575 amperes with an intensity of 46.7 volts. It is of the shunt-wound type of dynamo, built for the purpose of incandescent lighting; further than being of greater capacity, and having a hub made of the Cowles aluminum-brass which exhibited a tensile strength of 95,000 pounds per square inch and five per cent elongation, this dynamo does not differ from the ordinary machine.

Conduction of the Current of the Large Dynamo to the furnace in the furnace room and back to the machine, is accomplished by a complete metallic circuit except where it is broken by the interposition of carbon electrodes, and the mass of pulverized carbon in which the decomposition of the ore takes place. This circuit consists of thirteen copper wires each 0.3 inches in diameter. There is likewise inserted into this circuit an ampèremeter through whose helix the entire current flows, indicating, by its suction of a plunger armature attached to a spring balance and dial-faced indicator, the total strength of current being used.

This ampèremeter is an important element in the management of the furnace, as by the position of the finger on the dial the furnace attendant can tell to a nicety what is being done by the current within the furnace. It is placed upon a shelf in a good light, near to and in full view of a person in any position about the furnace.

Between the ammeter and the furnace in the furnace room, and forming part of the circuit, is placed a large resistance coil of german silver immersed in water, a heavy copper slide passing backward or forwards as desired, throwing more or less of this resistance into the circuit, and almost the entire energy of the current may be thus applied to heating water. The object of the resistance box is to serve as a safety appliance. It is used by the furnace operator when it is desired to change the current from one furnace to another, or if it be necessary to choke off the current almost entirely before breaking it by a switch, thus preventing serious flashing at the commutator of the dynamo or at the switch. It is likewise of value should any evidence of a short circuit appear in the furnace or elsewhere.

Thus far the apparatus that has been described, presents no novel feature beyond its great magnitude, the peculiar combination made, and the purpose for which it is used. Now, however, we will describe a device that we claim is something radically different from anything that has heretofore been known, namely, an incandescent electrical furnace for the smelting of refractory ores, metals and compounds, and in which other metallurgical and chemical operations, impossible in the past, may now be performed with both ease and economy. This furnace as constructed to utilize the current of the large dynamo, is a rectangular oblong box of fire-brick, with walls, bottom and ends, nine inches thick. The interior space being five feet long by one foot wide and one foot deep. This is closed by a cast-iron slab or cover through which are two three-inch holes for the

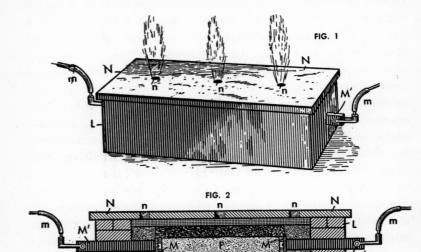

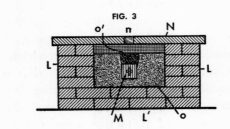

THE COWLES ELECTRIC SMELTING FURNACE.

Fig. 1   Perspective view.
Fig. 2   Longitudinal section.
Fig. 3   Transverse   "
L L'.   Fire-brick floor and walls.
N.   Removable fire-clay cover.
n.   Vents for escaping gases.

M M'.   Electrodes
m.   Conducting wires to dynamos
O.   Packing of fine charcoal.
P.   Charge of ore and granular charcoal.
O'.   Layer of granular charcoal, covering charge on top.

escape of the gases liberated during the operation. This lid may be removed at will, its own weight being all that is required to keep it in place. The walls of the furnace are designed to be air-tight. At both ends of the furnace are holes large enough to admit an enormous electric light carbon, three inches in diameter and thirty inches long. Each of these carbons is connected at the end, projecting outside of the furnace, with the positive or negative conductor as the case may be, the connection being a copper cap fitting over the end of the electrode, the same being fastened to a large and flexible wire cable which forms part of the circuit. When it is desired to charge the furnace, it is first necessary to lime it, to prevent its destruction by heat. To do this, a quantity of finely pulverized charcoal that has been soaked in a solution of lime and water, and then thoroughly dried in the drying pan, is put into the fire-brick box, enough being placed therein to cover the floor to a depth of several inches. The carbon electrodes are then pushed into the box through the end walls until the ends of the carbons are but a few inches apart. These electrodes are just on top of the finely powdered charcoal of the floor. A sheet-iron gauge or guard, parallelogram-shaped, and open at top and bottom, is now placed over these electrodes in such a manner as to form two walls on either side of the electrodes about three inches distant. Space is thus left between the sheet-iron and the walls of the furnace, and likewise for about a foot at each end of the same. More finely powdered limed charcoal is put into the furnace-box so as to completely fill the space outside the sheet-iron gauge and within the furnace walls and up to within a couple of inches of the top. The furnace is now almost entirely full of the lime-washed charcoal, except the space nine inches wide, three feet long and six inches deep in the centre of the box, and into which the electrodes project. All is now ready for

the charge, which is prepared. Should it be desired to produce aluminum-bronze, we mix sixteen or eighteen pounds
of granulated copper, twelve to fourteen pounds of aluminum oxide in the form of broken corundum, and several
pounds of coarsely broken charcoal together, and burying
the electrodes with the same, and thus filling the space inside the walls of the sheet-iron gauge. The gauge is then
lifted from the furnace, additional coarse charcoal is spread
over the entire mass, the iron top of box is put in place,
the seams luted with fire clay, the current from the dynamo
switched on, and the furnace is in operation in but little
more time than it has taken to give these apparently trifling
but very important details.

We will now proceed to make a little study of the phi-
losophy of the process, after first watching a successful "run"
or "heat" from the beginning to the close of the operation.
Of course, the furnace and its contents, when the current
of electricity was turned on, were entirely cold and the resistance presented to the flow of the current consequently is
higher than it would be at any time during the "heat," unless some unforeseen accident, such as a slight explosion of
gas, takes place. But notwithstanding that the furnace is cold,
a complete metallic circuit, with carbon tips dangerously
near together, is ready to convey a one hundred horse-power
flash of lightning into the furnace, should a short circuit
occur. *There are likewise many pounds of pure copper in
between and about these carbon tips that may be melted
and run together and thus produce a short circuit. With
these conditions an electrician would insist that the man in
charge of the furnace should look pretty sharply lest the
four-thousand dollar dynamo at the other end of the wire
be burned out, or somebody be injured by a heavy flash.*
The man in charge, however, has anticipated such a con-
tingency by having thrown in several coils of the resistance

box, so that under no condition, even if the great carbons in the furnace were pressed tight together, would the dynamo be able to produce a current of more than 1600 ampères, the maximum load. Upon watching the ampèremeter, however, it is seen that this precaution was not necessary for only about 200 ampères are indicated as flowing, the artificial resistance is therefore slightly diminished, the needle of the ammeter moves up rapidly to 600 or 800 ampères, suddenly it gives a jump up to 1,200, then back to 200, then with a bang the armature of the ammeter is brought against the magnet and it registers 1,600 ampères of current flowing, and then instantly drops back to almost zero.

As every jump of that needle means wear and tear on the commutator and brushes of the dynamo, care is now taken to keep more control of the current and a little more artificial resistance is thrown into the circuit. The needle now moves more slowly around the dial, gradually making fewer and fewer jumps, and at the end of eight or ten minutes, it has worked up to the 1,000 ampère mark, and becomes quite steady. Suddenly there is a hiss and a sharp report, a tongue of greenish yellow copper flame darts upwards from the hole in the furnace top and then disappears, to be followed after a minute or so by a slight vapor. This was caused by the monoxide of carbon combining with the atmosphere in the furnace to produce an explosive compound. To prevent this gas from accumulating to an extent to raise the furnace top and loosen the luting, the attendant holds a lighted stick over the vent and a series of slight explosions follow.

Soon a characteristic yellow-white flame appears, above the hole, the needle registers about 1,200 ampères of current flowing, all of the artificial resistance is withdrawn and the process of reducing aluminum and alloying it directly with copper is completely under way. Soon the needle gradually creeps around the dial to the 1,400 or 1,500 ampère mark. This is regarded as being a little too hot work for the dynamo and at the same time the plume of flame above the furnace indicates a little less rapid reduction. There are, therefore, two things now necessary. The first is to put more resistance into the circuit, and the second is to put more ore into the zone of reduction. These are both done by withdrawing one of the electrodes and the ammeter needle drops back to 1,200, and the flame above the furnace soon gives evidence of doing more work, by reason of more copious white fumes being given off.

This pulling out of the electrodes is repeated over and over again until both are out to their full length. At the end of an hour, the "heat" is completed. The current is then switched to another furnace, but one furnace being used at a heat. The artificial resistance is again resorted to, enough being thrown into the circuit gradually, thus slowly choking off the current, permitting the proper regulation of the brushes on the dynamo, and also giving time for the engine to govern itself. Finally, at the end of several minutes, the switch is thrown open and the furnace is entirely out of the circuit. Furnace No. 2 is now operated in precisely the same manner as the furnace No. 1, which is allowed to cool off. At the end of two hours furnace No. 2 is thrown out of the circuit and work begun on furnace No. 3. By this time No. 1 is ready to be discharged. The lid is removed and water is used with a sprinkling pot to quench the fire still remaining. At the bottom of the furnace, on the floor of fine charcoal, is found an oblong metallic and crystalline mass of white metal. It is the copper charged with from fifteen to thirty-five per cent. of aluminum and a small quantity of silicon. It frequently averages twenty per cent. to twenty-two per cent. of aluminum and silicon. Covering this mass is also found a considerable quantity of fused carbide of aluminum. Analysis of this product has shown thirty to sixty per cent. of metallic aluminum present. On cooling, it forms very large and distinct crystals.

The very rich white bronze is collected together, put into an ordinary graphite crucible, and run into ingots weighing fifty or sixty pounds. These are carefully analyzed by the chemist, after which they are remelted and copper is added to them in the proper proportion to reduce them to the standard ten per cent. aluminum-bronze. To guard against mistakes being made in the analysis of the white and brittle ingots in the amount of copper added thereto, and in keeping the bronze free from impurity, every ingot of ten per cent. aluminum-bronze has its tensile strength tested, and it must show a tenacity of at least 90,000 pounds to the square inch.

As to the capacity of our large dynamo, and the economy of the process, a few figures may be interesting. In ordinary circumstances we expect to average a daily production of at least 300 pounds of ten per cent. aluminum-bronze for twenty hours' work with each machine of this size. In addition to this 300 pounds of bronze, containing in round numbers thirty pounds of aluminum, there is produced about sixty pounds of metallic aluminum in the bye-products, a large portion of which, with proper concentrating apparatus, will be cheaply reclaimed and rendered marketable. Ninety pounds of aluminum in twenty hours is a production of four and one-half pounds per hour. Four and one-half pounds per hour produced by the energy of 120 horse-power equals the consumption of about 26.6 horse-power per hour to reduce one pound of aluminum. At times we have far exceeded this result. Indeed, two heats have been made wherein the energy consumed has been but twelve and one-half horse-power per hour per pound of metallic aluminum produced. Theoretically it should consume only about four and one-half horse-power per hour to effect the reduction, and in a new form of compound furnace to be built at our Lockport works, and in which 1,000 horse-power will be consumed, it is confidently expected that the output of bronze will not consume more than fifteen to twenty horse-power per hour for the reduction of one pound of aluminum.

Economy of the Process.—This may best be judged by the public in a general way from the fact that we are selling our ten per cent. aluminum-bronze as low in some instances as forty-five cents per pound net, and we are not selling it at a loss financially. This same bronze cannot be purchased elsewhere for less than $1.30 per pound. Our list price on ten per cent. bronze is sixty cents per pound.

The two and one-half per cent., five per cent. and seven and one-half per cent. bronzes are all proportionately less in cost. By the addition of zinc to the lower grades of aluminum-bronze an aluminum-brass is produced which is at once tough and malleable and of at least three times the tensile strength of ordinary brass. This brass has also vastly superior power to resist corrosion and oxidization. It can be made from the aluminum-bronze at a total cost of eighteen or twenty cents per pound.

Value of Electric Smelting.—"The Cowles Electric Smelting and Aluminum Company" claims that its process of electric smelting, within the next five or ten years, is destined to as completely revolutionize the brass and bronze trade of the world as the Bessemer converter has the iron and steel industry. This claim is based simply upon the ease and cheapness by which it can produce the alloys of aluminum and silicon, and the vast superiority of these alloys over any composition now in the market. It is further believed that cheap aluminum-bronze means a new era in warfare; that it insures a return to the age of bronze in the matter of heavy cannon, armor plates, gun carriages and small fire-arms. Why aluminum-bronze is the best metal for heavy guns is because sound, reliable and malleable castings can be made of at least fifty tons tensile strength per square inch, an endurance that far exceeds that of any forged iron or steel when made into heavy guns, and a finished gun of this kind can probably be manufactured in one-quarter of the time and at far less the cost of one made of steel. Heavy pieces of steel ordinance now cost from seventy-five cents to $1 per pound, require a vast plant for their production and a very long time for completion. The same guns made from aluminum-bronze could be cast in an ordinary foundry of sufficient capacity and finished in a lathe, thus avoiding all forging, welding, shrinking on of rings, tempering, drilling and annealing now required in the manipulation of heavy steel and iron cannons. Armor plates for heavy fortifications and ships could be made completely from cast metal, no machine work being required to finish them ready to go into place.

For cartridges, we believe that sheet aluminum-bronze will prove to be unrivalled by any composition now known, for it is the only cheap metal not affected chemically by gunpowder, and that in turn does not deteriorate the gun-powder when stored for a period of years. It is so strong, and so much less in specific gravity than brass or copper, that the cartridge shell may be made of one-half the weight now required. Aluminum-bronze is likewise most admirably adapted, on account of its enormous tenacity and stiffness and resistance to all forms of corrosion, for torpedo boat cylinders and steam boilers, seamless tubes, stay bolts, and particularly rivets, where great strength is required and there is any tendency to shear off the heads, for it is as easy to obtain fifty tons tensile strength in an aluminum-bronze rivet as it is twenty-five tons in iron.

The Future of the Process is one of great promise, and will undoubtedly lead to the production of cheap and pure aluminum itself within a very brief period. Indeed, "The Cowles Electric Smelting Company" asserts, on the back page of its pamphlet, that it expects to put the pure metal on the market within a year. When you are informed that we can charge iron, manganese, tin, copper, nickel, etc., with a very high percentage of metallic aluminum in this furnace, and that, also, without any base metal in the furnace, we can saturate the charcoal contained therein with metallic aluminum, most of which will be in a state of mechanical mixture with the carbon; and further, that we have produced specimens of aluminum ninety-nine per cent. pure in at least three different methods by the electric furnace; and that notwithstanding all this we have not made much of an effort in this direction, the majority of you will agree that the great problem of producing pure and cheap aluminum is practically solved. How cheap this method will be you may judge from the fact that, at our Lockport works, which will have a capacity of only two or three tons per day, we expect to produce the aluminum in bronze with the little silicon contained in it at a cost not to exceed forty cents per pound, or with copper at twelve cents per pound, the bronze will really cost but about fifteen cents per pound.

In truth, "The Cowles Electric Smelting and Aluminum Company" is founded upon the faith that ere long we shall be marketing pure aluminum at a cost not exceeding fifty or sixty cents per pound. An appreciation of how cheap this would be, can be had from the fact that one pound of aluminum would go about as far as three and one-half of copper, it being that much more bulky, and in reality it would be about as cheap as copper at eighteen cents per pound, without counting its vast superiority over copper for many purposes on account of its greater lightness and resistance to corrosive influence.

Thanking you, gentlemen, for your attention, I would respectfully call your attention to a collection of ore, carbon, white bronze, furnace products, specimens of sheet and wire, and other manufactures of aluminum-bronze, that I have brought with me for your inspection.

Litigation

The following is a list of the 16 judicial decisions and other court proceedings which are referred to at various points in the text. These fall into four groups: (1) to (6), litigation between the two Cowles companies and the Pittsburgh Reduction Company over alleged patent infringement; (7) to (9), contest between the Cowles Electric Smelting and Aluminum Company and Grosvenor P. Lowrey over ownership of the Bradley patents; (10) to (13), patent infringement action brought by the Electric Smelting and Aluminum Company (Cowles) against the Carborundum Company; (14) to (17), suits claiming anti-trust law violations brought by the United States Government against the Aluminum Company of America.

COWLES COMPANIES VS. PITTSBURGH REDUCTION COMPANY

1) Pittsburgh Reduction Company *vs.* Cowles Electric Smelting and Aluminum Company, in the Circuit Court of the Northern District of Ohio, Eastern Division, before Judge Taft, January 20, 1893 (55 Federal Reporter 301).

Issue: validity and infringement of Hall Patent No. 400,766, applied for July 9, 1886, issued April 2, 1889.

Disposition: Hall patent held valid and infringed by Cowles Electric Smelting and Aluminum Company.

2) Cowles Electric Smelting and Aluminum Company *vs.* Pittsburgh Reduction Company. Suit filed in 1891.

Issue: validity and infringement of Cowles Patent No. 319,795, applied for December 24, 1884, issued June 9, 1885.

Disposition: this suit was withdrawn by the Cowles Company in 1892 because doubt as to the validity of the Cowles patent was created by the unexpected issue on February 2, 1892, of Bradley Patent No. 468,148 for which the original application had been filed on February 23, 1883.

3) Pittsburgh Reduction Company *vs.* Cowles Electric Smelting and Aluminum Company, in the Circuit Court of the Northern District of Ohio, Eastern Division, before Judge Taft, November 9, 1894 (64 Federal Reporter 125).

Issue: motion to reopen the case to introduce new evidence and for a re-hearing.

Disposition: motion denied.

4) Electric Smelting and Aluminum Company (Cowles) *vs.* Pittsburgh Reduction Company, in the Circuit Court of the Western District of New York, before Judge Hazel, October 22, 1901 (111 Federal Reporter 742).

Issue: validity and infringement of Bradley patents Nos. 464,933 and 468,148, applied for February 23, 1883, issued December 8, 1891, and February 2, 1892, respectively.

Disposition: court held that the Bradley patents had not been infringed.

5) Pittsburgh Reduction Company *vs.* Cowles Electric Smelting and Aluminum Company, in the Circuit Court of the Northern District of Ohio, Eastern Division, before Judge Wing, April 4, 1903 (121 Federal Reporter 557).

Issue: petition to reopen, for newly-discovered evidence, Case (1) described above.

Disposition: petition granted.

6) Electric Smelting and Aluminum Company (Cowles) *vs.* Pittsburgh Reduction Company, in the Second Circuit Court of Appeals, New York State, before Judges Wallace, Lacombe, and Coxe, October 20, 1903 (125 Federal Reporter 926).

Issue: appeal from decision reported in Case (4) above, limited to Patent No. 468,148.

Disposition: held that the Bradley patent was valid and infringed by the Hall process as used by the Pittsburgh Reduction Company, reversing lower court.

COWLES COMPANY VS. LOWREY

7) Lowrey *vs.* Cowles Electric Smelting and Aluminum Company, in the Circuit Court of the Northern District of Ohio, Eastern Division, before Judge Taft, May 13, 1893 (56 Federal Reporter 488).

Issue: ownership of Bradley patents Nos. 464,933 and 468,148, plea to dispose of the matter in favor of the Cowles Company without trial.

Disposition: plea denied.

8) Lowrey *vs.* Cowles Electric Smelting and Aluminum Company, in the Circuit Court of the Northern District of Ohio, Eastern Division, before Judge Taft, April 23, 1895 (68 Federal Reporter 354).

Issue: ownership of Bradley patents.

Disposition: held that Bradley patents Nos. 464,933 and 468,148 were not covered by the contract between Bradley and the Cowles Company and were, therefore, the property of Lowrey.

9) Cowles Electric Smelting and Aluminum Company *vs.* Lowrey, in the Ohio Circuit Court of Appeals, Sixth Circuit, before Judge Severens, February 15, 1897 (79 Federal Reporter 331).

Issue: appeal from the decision of Judge Taft in Case (8) above.

Disposition: held that Bradley patents belonged to Cowles Company, reversing lower court.

COWLES COMPANY VS. CARBORUNDUM COMPANY

10) Electric Smelting and Aluminum Company (Cowles) *vs.* Carborundum Company, in the Circuit Court of the Western District of Pennsylvania, before Judge Buffington, July 26, 1897 (83 Federal Reporter 492).

Issue: validity and infringement of Cowles Patent No. 319,795, applied for December 24, 1884, issued June 9, 1885.

Disposition: court held that the Carborundum Company had not infringed the Cowles patent.

11) Electric Smelting and Aluminum Company (Cowles) *vs.* Carborundum Company, in the Circuit Court of Appeals, Third Circuit, Pennsylvania, before Judges Dallas, Gray, and Bradford, May 28, 1900 (102 Federal Reporter 618).

Issue: appeal from decision of Judge Buffington in Case (10) above.

Disposition: held that Carborundum Company had infringed Cowles patent, reversing lower court.

12) Electric Smelting and Aluminum Company (Cowles) *vs.* Carborundum Company, in the Circuit Court of the Western District of Pennsylvania, before Judge Buffington, November 24, 1900 (189 Federal Reporter 710).

Issue: case referred by court of appeals to lower court for determination of amount of damages.

Disposition: case referred by lower court to a master. About 12 years were consumed from 1900 to 1912 in the taking of testimony and determination of damages by the master, and in consideration of his recommendations by the lower court.

13) Carborundum Company *vs.* Electric Smelting and Aluminum Company (Cowles), Electric Smelting and Aluminum Company *vs.* Carborundum Company, in the Circuit Court of Appeals, Third Circuit, Pennsylvania, before Judges Bradford, Gray, and Young, March 15, 1913 (203 Federal Reporter 976).

Issue: appeal by Carborundum Company from findings of Judge Buffington in Case (12) above.

Disposition: Carborundum Company required to pay about $300,000 including damages, court and master's costs, and interest.

UNITED STATES VS. ALCOA

14) United States *vs.* Aluminum Company of America, in the United States District Court, Western District, Pennsylvania, before Judge Young, June 7, 1912 (consent decree).

Issue: alleged anti-trust law violations.

Disposition: annulment of agreement with European producers as to basis for sharing American and European markets; also annulment of various restrictive clauses in contracts between Alcoa and certain United States producers of bauxite, alumina, and fabricated aluminum products.

15) United States *vs.* Aluminum Company of America et al., in the United States District Court, Southern District, New York, before Judge Caffey, September 30 to October 10, 1941 (44 Federal Reporter Supplement 97).

Issue: action charging Alcoa with violation of provisions of the Sherman Act against monopolizing.

Disposition: the district court held for Alcoa and dismissed the bill.

16) United States *vs.* Aluminum Company of America et al., in the United States Circuit Court of Appeals, Second Circuit, before Judges L. Hand, Swan, and A. N. Hand, March 12, 1945 (148 Federal Second 416).

Issue: appeal of Case (15) above.

Disposition: on appeal, the lower court was reversed in part and the charge of monopolizing was sustained. A decree was ordered to enjoin "price squeeze" practices of Alcoa and to enjoin further cartel arrangements overseas.

17) United States *vs.* Aluminum Company of America et al., in the United States District Court, Southern District, New York, before Judge Knox, January 16, 1951 (91 Federal Supplement 333).

Issue: petition by Alcoa for a decree that the Company had ceased to monopolize the aluminum ingot market, and petition by the Government to have Alcoa divested of ownership of such of its properties as would be required to restore competitive conditions in the aluminum industry.

Disposition: nine principal Alcoa shareholders were required to divest themselves of their stock ownership, either in Alcoa or in Aluminium Limited. The court also held that certain "grant-back" provisions of patent licenses extended by Alcoa to its United States competitors were in violation of the Sherman Act and were therefore invalid and unenforceable.

Cowles Family Notes

The Genealogy of the Cowles Families in America, compiled by Colonel Calvin Duvall Cowles of Hartford, Connecticut, and published in 1929, is one of the most complete works of its kind in existence. Its 1502 pages include about 30,000 names and thousands of biographical sketches, and it traces the ancestry of all descendants of the family so far as the records permit.

There are several different branches of the Cowles family in the United States, three of them in Virginia which, on the basis of present information, cannot be traced to one ancestor, although a common origin is suggested by the fact that before the Revolutionary War they all lived north of the James River on or near the Chickahominy River in Charles City and James City counties about 10 to 20 miles northwest of Jamestown. The difficulty in determining this early history is largely due to the destruction of records during the Civil War. Colonel Cowles, compiler of the genealogy, believed that Richard Cowles, who bought 125 acres of land near Jamestown in 1614, was probably the progenitor of all branches of the Cowles family in Virginia and that he also had the distinction of being the first immigrant named Cowles of whom there is any record in America. It is possible that he was one of the 120 original settlers of

Jamestown in 1607 and he probably came from Gloucestershire, England.

The Virginia Cowleses were the first to establish themselves in this country, and for almost 350 years they have been represented among the influential citizens of that state. Nevertheless, the most prominent branch of the family in the United States today is the one which traces its ancestry to John Cowles, a farmer born in Gloucestershire, England, about 1598, who came to America shortly after he was 30 years old, about 8 years after the Pilgrims landed at Plymouth Rock and 14 years after the first recorded appearance of Richard Cowles in Virginia. John Cowles accompanied the Rev. Thomas Hooker on his pilgrimage from Cambridge, Massachusetts, to settle Hartford, Connecticut, in 1635. He moved in 1640 to a community about nine miles southwest of Hartford which four years later was incorporated and named Farmington. John Cowles could not write his own name but nevertheless served as a constable in Farmington, was reported to have been one of the seven "pillars" of the Congregational Church founded there in 1652, and in 1653-1654 represented the town in the General Assembly. He served as a juror in two Hartford witchcraft trials in 1662 and 1663 and died at Hatfield, Massachusetts, in 1675.

People bearing the name of Cowles, the original John and his descendants, have lived continuously in Farmington for 317 years. Among the early residents were Isaac Cowles (1675-1756) and Solomon Cowles (1719-1793), both of whom served in colonial days as captains in the military company, or "trainband," of Farmington. Residents of that community who took part in the Revolutionary War included Lieutenant Colonel Isaac Cowles (1756-1837), who fought in various engagements including the battle of Saratoga, and Major General Solomon Cowles (1758-1846) who while an 18-year-old undergraduate at Princeton College in 1776 enlisted in a company which opposed the march of the British through New Jersey. He then joined the American army under General George Washington and participated in five additional battles, being present at the surrender of General Burgoyne at Saratoga. After the Revolutionary War he attended both Yale and Harvard colleges for brief periods and during the War of 1812 commanded a force of 3000 soldiers raised by the state of Connecticut. Three other Farmington members of the family who served in the army during the War of 1812 were Colonel Martin Cowles (1774-1844), Major General George Cowles (1780-1860), and Major Timothy Cowles (1784-1858), the latter having been a member of the corporation of Yale College and owner of a hotel building which later was taken over by the girls' school, founded by Miss Sarah Porter, which has always been known simply as Farmington.

Rear Admiral Walter Cleveland Cowles (1853-1917) of Farmington graduated from the United States Naval Academy at Annapolis in 1873. He commanded the cruiser "Brooklyn" in 1901 and was in command of the battleship "Kentucky" during a round-the-world cruise. His last assignment was in 1915 as commander-in-chief of the Asiatic Fleet. His older brother, Rear Admiral William Sheffield Cowles (1846-1923) graduated at Annapolis in 1867. He was naval attaché at the American Embassy in London (1893-1897), in command of the cruiser "Topeka" during 1898, naval aide to President McKinley in 1899, and in command of the battleship "Missouri" (1903-1905), having served at various times in Mediterranean, North Atlantic, Pacific, and Asiatic stations. His wife, Anna, was a sister of President Theodore Roosevelt. Their son, William Sheffield Cowles (1898-   ), a member of the Council of Yale University and chairman of the committee on its Peabody Museum, is at present living in the Cowles homestead, "Old Gate," at Farmington.

Twenty-five individuals bearing the name of Cowles have been listed in *Who's Who in America* since it was first published in 1899.[1] Two of these came from Virginia branches of the family but the remaining 23 were all descendants of the original John Cowles of Farmington. In addition to the two admirals, these include six descendants of Dr. Edwin Weed Cowles (1794-1861) of Cleveland and four of the Des Moines, Iowa, Cowles family.

Both of these families have had several members identified with newspaper publishing, the Edwin Weed Cowles branch being represented by Edwin Cowles (1825-1890), publisher of the *Cleveland Leader* and *Cleveland Evening News;* Alfred Cowles (1832-1889), business manager of the *Chicago Tribune,* and a director of the Tribune Company; Alfred Cowles (1866-1939), a director of the Tribune Company and affiliated corporation, publishers of the *Chicago Tribune* and *New York News;* William Hutchinson Cowles (1866-1946), publisher of the Spokane *Spokesman-Review* and *Spokane Chronicle,* and of the *Washington Farmer, Oregon Farmer,* and *Idaho Farmer,* and for more than 30 years a director of the Associated Press; Alfred Cowles (1891-   ), a director of the Tribune Company and affiliated corporations; William Hutchinson Cowles (1902-   ), the present publisher of the two Spokane newspapers and four affiliated farm papers, and a director of the Associated Press and Inter-American Press Association, and formerly

[1] This total excludes two women, listed in *Who's Who* under Cowles, who acquired the name by marriage. One of these is Fleur Fenton, former wife of Gardner Cowles (1903-   ), and the other Julia Darrow (1862-1919) who married Francis Dana Cowles, both of these Cowles husbands being descended from the original John Cowles of Farmington, Connecticut.

president and a director of the Agricultural Publishers Association.

The Des Moines branch of the family includes Gardner Cowles (1861-1946), formerly board chairman of the Register and Tribune Company, publisher of the *Des Moines Register* and *Des Moines Tribune;* his son John Cowles (1898-   ), board chairman of the Des Moines Register and Tribune Company, Cowles Magazines, Inc., publisher of *Look* and *Quick* magazines, president of the Minneapolis Star and Tribune Company, publisher of the *Minneapolis Star* and *Minneapolis Tribune,* formerly a director of the Audit Bureau of Circulation and of the Associated Press; another son Gardner Cowles (1903-   ), president of the Des Moines Register and Tribune Company and Cowles Magazines, Inc.

The coincidence of so many people by the name of Cowles being identified with the newspaper business has frequently led to the assumption that the Des Moines-Minneapolis group is closely related to the Chicago-Spokane contingent. This, however, is not correct. Contemporary members of the two branches of the family are eight generations removed from their nearest common ancestor, the John Cowles who came to America about 1628. In other words, the present John and Gardner Cowles are seventh cousins of the present Alfred and William Hutchinson Cowles. William Sheffield Cowles 3rd, son of William Sheffield Cowles now living in the Farmington homestead, is also a seventh cousin of John and Gardner Cowles. He is a fifth cousin of Alfred and William Hutchinson Cowles.

The chart on page 233 lists 30 descendants of Dr. Edwin Weed Cowles and Judge Mosely Hutchinson, at least 50 percent of whose ancestry is identical with that of Eugene H. and Alfred H. Cowles. Two of these 30 were, of course, the father and mother of the two inventors. Ten of the remaining 28 were their aunts and uncles. There were also two sisters, a brother, and three double first cousins.[2] The members of that generation, among them, had 12 children, eight of whom are living today.

One of the inventors' uncles, Judge Samuel Cowles (1823-1880), attended Western Reserve College in Ohio. He studied law in Cleveland and was there admitted to the bar in 1846. In 1852 he went by sea around the Horn to California. During 1856 he became a member of the famous vigilance committee which rescued the San Francisco city government from the domination of gamblers and thieves. At that time, according to the *Encyclopedia Americana,* ". . . the city was so overrun with the lawless element among the miners and adventurers that the administration of justice in the hands of the constituted authorities was a travesty. It was then that the work of the vigilance committee, or Vigilantes, as they were styled, began. That work was short, sharp, and terrible. Thieves and murderers were hanged on every side, while others were forced to seek safety in flight." [3]

In 1856 Samuel Cowles was elected police judge by the law and order party of the city and in 1860 he was elected on the Republican ticket as judge of the court of common pleas. He held that post for eight years during which time only three of his many important decisions were reversed by the court of appeals. Once in later years, when a breakdown of constituted authority was imminent during the railroad strikes of 1877, he was named a member of the committee of safety composed of 25 leading citizens of San Francisco in whose hands protection of the city was placed.

[2] The two brothers, Edwin Cowles (1825-1890) and Alfred Cowles (1832-1889), married two sisters, Elizabeth Caroline Hutchinson (1827-1910) and Sarah Frances Hutchinson (1837-1884). The children of these two couples were, therefore, double first cousins.

[3] *Encyclopedia Americana,* 1955 ed., Vol. 28, p. 84.

Helen Cowles (1821-1892), an aunt of the inventors, graduated from Oberlin College in 1843, prior to which date very few women in the world had received college educations. She married Dr. Franklin C. Markham in 1845 and five years after that he died on the British bark, "Change," during a voyage from Panama to San Francisco. They had two sons, Franklin L. Markham and Edwin Cowles Markham, who enlisted in the Northern Army during the Civil War at the ages of 15 and 16, respectively. Edwin, the older of the two, was in 65 engagements during the war and at its end, when about 20 years of age, held the rank of lieutenant and brevet captain.

A sister of the inventors, Helen Hutchinson Cowles (1851-1884) married George Potwin Pomeroy (1837-1887) who for many years was secretary of the United States Legation at Paris and also held the post of consul general at Cairo, Egypt.

The original Cowles Electric Smelting and Aluminum Company, founded in 1885 by Edwin Cowles and his two inventor sons, was reorganized in 1895 as the Electric Smelting and Aluminum Company with Alfred H. Cowles as its president. Between 1900 and 1910 he was working in a pilot plant at Sewaren, New Jersey, on the development of a process which he hoped would be an improvement over the existing method of extracting alumina from clay. This process never became a commercial success but while experimenting with it in 1908 he stumbled on an alkaline substance with excellent detergent properties. From this discovery was developed a profitable business in the laundry and metal cleaning fields with a product the dominant ingredient of which was sodium metasilicate which had previously been known to science, but not developed commercially. This product was marketed by the Cowles Detergent Company which in 1927 absorbed the Electric Smelting and Aluminum Company. Detergent silicates in various forms are now widely used in cleaning compounds. The name Cowles Detergent Company was changed to Cowles Chemical Company in 1948 and the latter, with offices in Cleveland, is today one of the leading manufacturers of cleaning compounds containing detergent silicates.

Lewis Hutchinson Cowles (1861-1939), a brother of the inventors, had a son, Edwin (1892-   ) who received an engineering degree from Cornell University in 1916 and in World War I was a lieutenant, senior grade, in the United States Navy, serving with destroyer forces in European waters. He was president of the Cowles Chemical Company and its predecessor, The Cowles Detergent Company, from 1941 to 1952. A grandnephew, Charles C. Bassett, is today vice president and director of sales.

The Chicago branch of the family was founded by an uncle of the inventors, Alfred Cowles (1832-1889), who went there from Cleveland in 1855 with Joseph Medill. They purchased the *Chicago Tribune* and Alfred Cowles became its business manager as well as a director of the Tribune Company, which posts he held until his death in 1889. In 1866 he also was elected a director of the Commercial National Bank, incorporated in that year, which through mergers became what is today the Continental Illinois National Bank and Trust Company of Chicago, one of the largest banks in the United States.

The oldest son of Alfred Cowles (1832-1889) was Alfred Cowles (1865-1939) who graduated from Yale University in 1886. While there he rowed on the crew for three years, being captain in his senior year. His crew, in its race with Harvard at New London in 1884, established a new downstream four-mile record of 20 minutes and 30¾ seconds, and in 1886 his crew established the upstream record of 20 minutes and 41¼ seconds which stood for 40 years. In the 1886 race Alfred Cowles, 6 feet 1½ inches tall, weighed 169½ pounds, and his record-breaking crew, one of the lightest ever to row at Yale, averaged only 161 pounds in weight. He had a fine baritone voice which was thought to have been good enough for grand opera, had he chosen to make singing his profession. After graduation from Yale he studied law and in 1889 was admitted to the Illinois Bar. For many years he was a director of the American Radiator Company and from 1907 until his death in 1939 he was a director of the Continental Illinois National Bank and Trust Company of Chicago and its predecessor banks. For 49 years he was a director of the Tribune Company, serving at one time as its secretary and treasurer. It was largely due to his influence that in 1911 Robert Rutherford McCormick and Joseph Medill Patterson, grandsons of Joseph Medill, were installed as co-editors of the *Chicago Tribune.* Under their leadership it achieved the largest daily and Sunday circulation of any standard-sized newspaper in the United States, and the tabloid *New York News,* three years after it was founded in 1919, acquired the largest circulation of any newspaper in this country. To this day both papers maintain the same rating, the *Tribune's* circulation being second only to that of the *News.*

Three generations of Cowleses have been directors of the Tribune Company and, except for the year 1890, an Alfred Cowles has been on that board continuously since the present company elected its original board of directors in 1864. Actually, the first Cowles became business manager and a principal owner of the *Chicago Tribune* in 1855. The same succession of three Alfred Cowleses has also been on the directorate of the Continental Illinois National Bank and Trust Company of Chicago and its predecessor banks for most of the 91 years since 1866.

The second son of Alfred Cowles (1832-1889) was William Hutchinson Cowles (1866-1946). In 1877, at 11 years of age, while attempting to climb the side ladder on a freight car of a moving train on the Chicago lake front near his home, he fell under the wheels and lost his left leg below the knee. Aided by an artificial leg he was later able to skate and ride a bicycle and a horse. He graduated from Yale University in 1887 where he was editor-in-chief of the student newspaper, the *Yale Daily News*. He completed the Yale Law School course in 1889 and was in that year admitted to the Connecticut Bar. Shortly thereafter his father died and he returned to Chicago where he went to work as a police reporter on the *Tribune*. At that time Joseph French Johnson, its financial editor, with two other associates on the *Tribune* migrated to Spokane, Washington, where in 1890 they started a daily morning newspaper, the *Spokesman,* in competition with the existing morning paper, the *Review,* which was controlled by a group of Portland men.

In July, 1891, William H. Cowles joined Johnson and the others in their Spokane venture. Before long a depression hit the country and by January, 1893, the combined losses of the *Review* and *Spokesman* were $10,000 a month. At that point the associates of W. H. Cowles on the *Spokesman* decided that they had lost enough, and he made a deal with the three owners of the *Review* whereby publication of the *Spokesman* was discontinued on February 19, 1893, and for $24,000 he got a one-quarter interest in the *Review* which included liability for one-quarter of the $80,000 mortgage on the Review Building. Johnson went east, later becoming dean of the School of Commerce at New York University. Meanwhile the depression deepened and the three Portland associates became so discouraged that in June, 1894, they gave their interest in the *Review* to W. H. Cowles on condition that he assume full liability for the $80,000 mortgage. The new owner changed the paper's name to *Spokesman-Review* because there had been great opposition to the old

Review due to its editorial policy having been dictated from Portland.

The new regime was greeted with enthusiasm by residents of Spokane and the surrounding territory, but it was four years more before the *Spokesman-Review* ceased to lose money. For seven years following his arrival in Spokane during the summer of 1891 William H. Cowles had found it necessary to call on his brother, Alfred, for advances against his share of his father's estate which was administered by a board of trustees in Chicago. It was with considerable relief, therefore, that on October 30, 1898, Alfred wrote to his younger brother expressing great pleasure at the termination of the long-standing and regular flow of payments from Chicago which before they ended had absorbed practically all of the Spokane publisher's inheritance.

William H. Cowles first became a director of the Associated Press in 1911 and continued in that capacity until his resignation in 1944. He served as second vice-president in 1937 and as first vice-president in 1938. During his 33 years incumbency the Board was composed of from 15 to 18 directors and for much of that time he was the only one from the northwestern United States, a region comprising the states of Washington, Oregon, Idaho, Montana, and Wyoming, which in area constitutes about one-sixth of the country and today includes about 5,500,000 people. In 1935 he received an LL.D. degree from Whitman College in Walla Walla, Washington.

At his death in 1946, William H. Cowles was publisher of the *Spokesman-Review,* only morning newspaper in Spokane, and of the *Spokane Chronicle,* its leading evening newspaper, purchased by him in 1897. He was the publisher of three semi-monthly farm papers, the *Washington Farmer, Oregon Farmer,* and *Idaho Farmer.* He also owned a Spokane radio station and extensive real estate and other properties there and elsewhere. In 1945 he gave to Whitworth College of Spokane a library in memory of his wife and in 1956 his children gave to Whitworth an auditorium in memory of him.

Alfred Cowles (1865-1939) and William Hutchinson Cowles (1866-1946) married two sisters, Elizabeth Cheney (1865-1898) and Harriet Bowen Cheney (1867-1938), daughters of Knight Dexter Cheney (1837-1907), president of Cheney Brothers silk mills in Manchester, Connecticut. The children of these two families are, therefore, double first cousins.

Sarah Frances Cowles (1862-1945), daughter of Alfred Cowles (1832-1889), married Philip Battell Stewart (1865-1957) of Middlebury, son of John Wolcott Stewart (1825-1915), United States senator and governor of Vermont. Philip B. Stewart was a Yale, 1886, roommate of his future brother-in-law, Alfred Cowles, and was captain of the Yale 1886 intercollegiate champion baseball team. Having practiced law for a number of years in Boston, he and his family moved in 1898 to Colorado Springs where for many years he was active in politics. On one occasion, shortly after the turn of the century, he was nominated as Republican candidate for governor of Colorado but withdrew from the race as a result of illness. He was a friend of Theodore Roosevelt and, while the latter was president of the United States, organized and accompanied him in 1901 and 1903 on two bear and lion hunting trips in Colorado. Philip B. Stewart received LL.D. degrees from Middlebury (Vermont) College in 1939 and from Colorado College in 1940. He was an authority on the early history of the west and on natural history of the Rocky Mountain region.

Sarah Frances Cowles Stewart in 1940 established in memory of her mother the Sarah Frances Hutchinson Cowles Fund which currently awards each year about 90 scholarships averaging $300, and ranging from $100 to $900 each, to young women who otherwise would be unable to afford a college education. She also in 1928 participated with her two brothers, Alfred and William Hutchinson Cowles, in donating $500,000 to establish at Yale University in memory of their father the Alfred Cowles Foundation for the Study of Government.

Since 1932 various members of the family have combined to support the work of the Cowles Commission for Research in Economics. From the time it was founded the Commission has served as headquarters for the Econometric Society, an international society devoted to the advancement of economic theory in its relation to statistics and mathematics. For the last 25 years Alfred Cowles (1891-   ) has been treasurer of the Society and president of the Commission. The main object of the Econometric Society is to promote studies that aim at a unification of the theoretical-quantitative and empirical-quantitative approach to economic problems and that are penetrated by constructive and rigorous thinking similar to that which has come to dominate in the natural sciences. The Society has about 1700 members and 900 library subscribers located in about 75 different countries of the world.

The depression of the 1930s served as the background from which the Cowles Commission and the Econometric Society emerged. In the fall of 1929, after eight years of almost continuous bull markets, the United States was struck by the initial onslaught of the most devastating economic collapse this country has ever known. The stock market, as measured by the Dow Jones average of 30 leading industrial stocks, fell 50 percent in a little over two months. There followed a brief rally, lasting about six months, and then a renewed decline which by the middle of 1932 carried the Dow Jones industrial average down to less than

11 percent of its September, 1929, high. This record-breaking shrinkage in market values was accompanied by such other phenomena as a decline of 85 percent in steel production, an increase in unemployment to almost 28 percent of the labor force, and by the bank moratorium. Economists, in general, had not foreseen this catastrophe nor, when it occurred, were they ready with any remedy which the leaders of that time were willing to adopt. To many observers it seemed that economics was discredited and that something fundamental would have to be done if economists were ever to provide useful guidance which would be taken seriously by business and political leaders. Against this background, in the hope that a more scientific approach would be helpful, the Cowles Commission for Research in Economics and the Econometric Society were founded.

The Cowles Commission for the first seven years of its existence had its headquarters in Colorado Springs. From 1939 to 1955 it was at the University of Chicago and since then it has been at New Haven, Connecticut, where the work is being carried on under the name "Cowles Foundation for Research in Economics at Yale University." The Cowles Commission has published 18 books, and more than 100 papers of importance in scientific journals, reporting the results of research done by members of its staff in the fields of statistics and econometrics. Also the Econometric Society, subsidized by the Cowles Commission, has published 25 annual volumes of its quarterly journal, *Econometrica*. In addition to contributions from members of the family, substantial grants for work conducted by the Cowles Commission have been made in recent years by the Rockefeller Foundation, Office of Naval Research, and RAND Corporation (civilian research organization of the United States Air Corps). The University of Chicago and Yale University have also contributed various valuable facilities.

The word "econometrics" was originated in 1930 by the founders of the Econometric Society. Today there are articles on econometrics in *Collier's Encyclopedia* and the *Encyclopedia Americana* both of which also mention the work of the Cowles Commission for Research in Economics. The Commission published in 1952 a 180-page report covering its first 20 years. Professor Kenneth E. Boulding of the University of Michigan wrote a review of this report which was published in *Kyklos*, a Swiss journal devoted to the social sciences. In it he said:

Occasionally there springs up in the academic community extraordinary "cells" of ideas and research of such life and vitality that their influence reaches out into the whole world of the intellect. Such, for instance, was the group of economists at the University of Vienna at the close of the last century, or the group at Cambridge University between the world wars. It is becoming more and more clear that the Cowles Commission and the leaders of the Econometric Society constitute such a group in the present day, in the sense that no economist anywhere in the world can afford to remain completely ignorant of the ferment of ideas, the new research techniques and new points of view which are constantly proceeding from the activities which center in a few rooms in the Social Science Building at the University of Chicago. Econometrics has been one of the most significant "growing points" of economics in the past twenty years. It is not however a "school" in the sense of the "Austrian School," contending for the supremacy of its theoretical position against other schools, so much as a "movement," finding its bond of unity in the common skills and methods of its adherents rather than in any uniformity of theoretical position. The nerve center of this world movement is unquestionably the Cowles Commission, and the report on their first twenty years of work is therefore of peculiar interest. . . . Not the least interesting part of the report (is) an appendix which consists of brief biographies of all people who have been associated with the work of the Commission since its foundation. This appendix reads almost like an international "Who's Who" of economics, and is a striking testimony to the world-wide impact of the Commission . . .

The guiding idea behind the work of the Commission has been the *interaction* of theory and measurement in economics-theory guiding attempts at measurement, and measurement in turn profoundly modifying theory, forcing it into forms which it would never have taken had it not been for the exacting requirements imposed by the quantitative method. In this respect the Cowles Commission differs somewhat from the work of the other great American economic research agency—the National Bureau for Economic Research, where emphasis has been on the collection and description of economic data rather than on the close interaction of theory and measurement. It would be unjust to describe the work of the National Bureau as measurement without theory, nevertheless the antitheoretical biases of Wesley Mitchell inevitably left a stamp on the work of the Bureau, in the sense that its work is not so much *economic* theory as theory of measurement and description. For this reason the present writer at least cannot escape the impression that, valuable as the work of the National Bureau has been, the work of the Cowles Commission has surpassed it in quality, and has made a much greater impact on the development of economic thought and knowledge. . . .

It is impossible to summarize what is in itself a summary, but I hope I have said enough to justify the proposition that when the history of economic thought in the twentieth century comes to be written, the work of the members of the Cowles Commission will occupy a large part of the book.

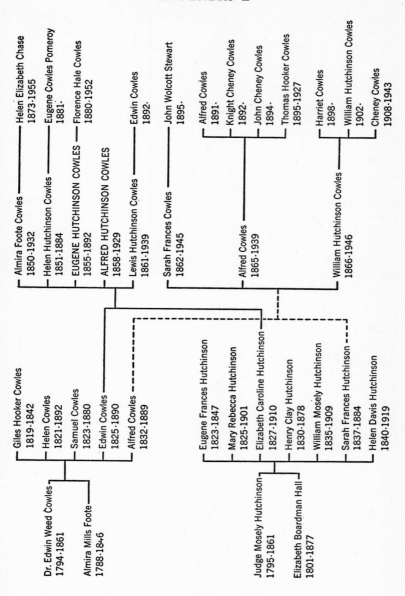

Bibliography

Acheson, E. G., *Pathfinder, Discovery, Invention, Industry,* New York, The Press Scrap Book, 1910.

Adams, Edward Dean, *Niagara Power—History of Niagara Falls Power Company,* 1886-1918, privately printed for Niagara Falls Power Company by Bartlett Orr Press, New York, 1927.

Allen, E. P., "The Production of Aluminum," *Cassier's Magazine,* February, 1892, pages 297-304.

"Aluminum Empire," *Fortune,* June, 1954, pages 103-12, 221, 222, and 225.

Aluminum, the Industry and the Four North American Producers, First Boston Corporation, New York, 1951.

Anderson, R. J., *The Metallurgy of Aluminium and Aluminium Alloys,* New York, H. C. Baird & Co., 1925.

Borchers, Wilhelm, *Electric Smelting and Refining,* translation of third German edition with additions by Walter G. McMillan, London, C. Griffin & Co., 1904.

——, *Electric Furnaces,* translation of second German edition by Henry G. Solomon, 2nd English ed., London, Longmans, Green & Co., 1908.

Budgen, N. F., *Aluminium and Its Alloys, Their Production, Properties and Application,* London, Pitman & Sons, 1933.

Carr, C. C., *Alcoa, An American Enterprise,* New York, Rinehart & Co., Inc., 1952.

Cowles, Eugene H., "The Production of Aluminum and Its Alloys in the Electric Furnace," *Journal of the Franklin Institute of Philadelphia,* February, 1886, pages 111-22.

Edwards, Junius, *The Immortal Woodshed,* New York, Dodd, Mead & Co., 1955.

——, *Alfred E. Hunt, A Captain in Industry,* New York, printed privately, 1957.

Edwards, J. D., Frary, F. C., and Jeffries, Zay, *The Aluminum Industry,* New York, McGraw-Hill Book Co., 1930. 2 vols.

Engle, Nathanael H., Gregory, Homer E., and Mossé, Robert, *Aluminum*, Chicago, Richard D. Irwin, Inc., 1945.

Hammond, John Winthrop, *Men and Volts, the Story of General Electric*, New York, J. B. Lippincott Co., 1941.

Hartford, W. J., *Alfred H. Cowles, Pioneer of Electric Smelting and the Aluminum Process of Today*, New York, Writers Press Association, 1927.

History of the British Aluminium Company Limited, 1894-1955, London, Norfolk House, 1955.

Hobbs, D. B., *Aluminum*, Milwaukee, Bruce Publishing Co., 1938.

Holbrook, Stewart H., *The Age of the Moguls*, Garden City, New York, Doubleday & Co., 1954.

Holmes, H. N., *Fifty Years of Industrial Aluminum*, Oberlin, Ohio, Oberlin College, 1937. (Bulletin of Oberlin College, New Series No. 346.)

Kershaw, John B. C., *Electro-metallurgy*, New York, D. Van Nostrand Co., 1908.

Love, Philip H., *Andrew W. Mellon, The Man and His Work*, Baltimore, Maryland, F. Heath Coggins & Co., 1929.

Mastick, Seabury, "Chemical Patents," *Journal of Industrial and Engineering Chemistry*, October, 1915, pages 879-82; November, 1915, pages 986-91; December, 1915, pages 1071-81.

Metcalfe, June, *Aluminum from Mine to Sky*, New York, Whittlesey House, 1947.

Minet, Adolphe, *The Production of Aluminum*, translation with additions by Leonard Waldo, New York, J. Wiley & Sons, 1905.

Mortimer, George, *Aluminum, Its Manufacture, Manipulation, and Marketing*, New York, Pitman & Sons, 1920.

Muller, Charlotte, *Light Metals Monopoly*, New York, Columbia University Press, 1946.

National Cyclopedia of American Biography, Alfred Hutchinson Cowles —A Biographical Sketch, New York, James T. White & Co., 1916.

O'Connor, Harvey, *Mellon's Millions*, New York, John Day Co., 1933.

Parsons, R. H., *Early Days of the Power Station Industry*, Cambridge, England, Cambridge University Press, 1940.

Passer, H. C., *The Electrical Manufacturers, 1875-1890*, Cambridge, Harvard University Press, 1953.

Pattison, J. T., *The Manufacture of Aluminum*, New York, Spon & Chamberlain, 1918.

Perry, Josephine, *The Light Metals Industry*, New York, Longmans, Green & Co., 1947.

Pring, J. N., *The Electric Furnace*, London, Longmans, Green & Co., 1921.

BIBLIOGRAPHY

Richards, J. W., *Aluminium: Its History, Occurrence, Properties, Metallurgy and Applications, Including its Alloys,* 3rd ed. rev., Philadelphia, H. C. Baird & Co., 1896.

U.S. Patent Office Interference Testimony, Fauré *vs.* Bradley and Crocker *vs.* Cowles and Cowles, November and December, 1888, and January, 1889.

Wallace, D. H., *Market Control in the Aluminum Industry,* Cambridge, Harvard University Press, 1937. (Harvard Economic Studies, Vol. 58.)

Index

Acetylene gas, 44

Acheson, Edward G., 44-47; claims to have discovered carborundum, 46

Acheson Graphite Co., 45; uses Cowles electric furnace, 45; acquires Uihlein bauxite deposits, 116-17

Alcoa. *See* Aluminum Co. of America

Allgemeine Electrizitats-Gesellschaft, 94

Alumina, difficulties in treatment of, 4; how they were overcome, 16-17; cryolite bath proposed by Hall and Héroult, 64

Aluminium Industrie Aktiengesellschaft, 94

Aluminium Limited, incorporation of, 111; function of, 111

Aluminum, relative importance of, 1; first introduction to public, 2; first extensive commercial use of, 2, 14; characteristics of, 2; weight relative to other metals, 2; commercial uses for, 2; relative abundance in earth's crust, 3-4; electrolysis of aqueous solutions, 5; first isolation of, 5-6; first electrolytic production of, 7; early commercial status of, 8; importance of modern process, 18

Aluminum alloys, early British production dominated by Cowles brothers, 93, 95

Aluminum bronze, price cut two-thirds by Cowles brothers, 35; Berlin investors become interested in, 93

Aluminum Co. of America, successor to Pittsburgh Reduction Co., vii; reasons given by its representatives for Hall's early failures, 74; Pittsburgh Reduction Co. changes name to, 110; estimate of 1909 earnings, 112; Richard B. Mellon serves as president of, 112; defendant in federal antitrust suit, 112-13; acquires bauxite deposits, 112-13; restrictive agreements, 112-13; U.S. charge that it controlled bauxite deposits, 113; denies monopoly of bauxite deposits, 113; restrictive agreements annulled, 113; purchases Southern Aluminium Co., 115; acquires Uihlein bauxite deposits, 116-17; defendant in world's longest trial, 118; wins victory in lower court monopoly suit, 118; loses U.S. appeal of monopoly suit, 118-19; connection with Aluminium Limited severed, 118-19; principal shareholders sell Aluminium Limited stock, 118-19; outlines of court contests with U.S. Government, 215-16. *See also* Pittsburgh Reduction Co.

Aluminum Co. of America stock,

239

INDEX

estimate of its value at Hall's death, 104

Aluminum industry, importance to it of electric furnace, 48

Aluminum monopoly, established by Taft injunction, 111; termination of, 117-18; its adverse effect on Cowles prestige, 126

Aluminum oxide. *See* alumina

Aluminum prices, history compared with copper and steel, 2; reduced by Deville, 8; reduced by modern process, 14; Hall and Cowles brothers responsible for great reduction, 62; great reduction occurs before issue of Bradley patents, 62; first reduced to 50 cents per pound, 85, 99; boosted by Taft's decision, 99; chart covering period 1852-1957, 128

Aluminum production, popular belief regarding origin of modern process, vii; sources of information regarding origin of modern process, vii-viii; world increase in, 2; increase relative to other metals, 3; technical difficulties in, 4; invention of modern process, 15; modern process not originated by any one man, 18; modern process not fully described in any one patent, 19-20; processes originated by Cowles brothers, 36; Cowles brothers try modern process before meeting Hall, 69; increase in 1893-1903 decade, 111; output of leading North American companies, 119; chart covering period 1887-1956 for North America, 129; chart covering period 1925-1956 for world, 130

Anderson, Robert J., 40

Apaches, 29-30

Arc light, first demonstration of, 9-10; creates need for larger dynamos, 10-11

Arnold, Thurman, prosecutes Alcoa, 118

Badin, Adrian, organizes Southern Aluminium Co., 114

Baldwin, Dudley, describes Hall's small crucibles, 73; says Hall's Lockport experiments were unsuccessful, 78

Bauxite, Bayer process for extracting alumina from, 95

Bayer, Karl Joseph, 95

Bell, Alexander Graham, invention of telephone by, 9

Berlin investors, make offer for Cowles European patent rights, 93

Billy the Kid, 29

Boguski, Joseph, Cowles Co. acquires his patent, 41, 67; his achievements, 41-42; importance of his contribution cited by U.S. patent examiner, 41-42; similarity of his process to Hall's, 42; first to propose addition of simple alumina to cryolite bath, 67; text of his British patent, 149-53; mentioned, 123

Bonney, William. *See* Billy the Kid

Bradley, Charles Schenck, his part in originating modern aluminum process, 15; Cowles brothers' only rival in electric-furnace idea, 51; his patent contest with Cowles brothers, 52-53; uncertainty as to when he conceived electric-furnace idea, 55-56; his complex legal status versus Cowles brothers, 58-59; text of Bradley-Crocker patent, 162-70; mentioned, 123, 125-26. *See also* Bradley patent

Bradley Electric Power Co., 51-52

Bradley patent, a "paper" one, 18, 58-59; feature of modern aluminum process not covered by, 19-20; rights sold to Cowles Co., 52, 102; application for, 53; Pittsburgh Reduction Co. held to have infringed it, 56, 102-3; application filed after Cowles brothers conceived idea, 59; application filed before Cowles

240

Faraday, Michael, pioneering work on dynamo, 9; mentioned, 123
Fauré, Camille A., 54
Ford, Henry, 110
Franklin Institute, Eugene H. Cowles describes Cowles electric furnace at meeting of, 34; awards medal to Cowles brothers, 37; comments on achievements of Cowles brothers, 37
Franklin Institute Journal, says Cowles brothers invented electric furnace, 36; text of paper describing Cowles electric furnace, 197-209

Garrett, Sheriff Pat, 29
General Chemical Co., restrictive contract with Alcoa, 113
General Electric Co., takes over Bradley Electric Power Co., 51-52
General Electric historian, says Cowles brothers invented electric furnace, 36-37; describes Bradley's converter, 51
Geronimo, 29
Gramme, Z. T., helps develop dynamo, 9; mentioned, 123
Grätzel, Dr. Richard, his soluble anode patent, 67

Hall, Charles Martin, credited with originating modern aluminum process, vii, 86; chief inventor for Pittsburgh Reduction Co., vii; his part in originating modern aluminum process, 15; technicalities in U.S. patent law give him advantage over Héroult, 64-65; early life, 65; his first patent application divided, 67; his arguments in favor of copper anodes, 71-72; reasons given by Alcoa historians for his early failures, 74; lengthy negotiations with Patent Office, 75;

claims discovery that cryolite dissolves alumina freely, 81; originally employed unworkable process at Pittsburgh Reduction Co., 83; his letter rejecting simple cryolite bath, 84; his first use of modern aluminum process, 86-87; stock holdings in Pittsburgh Reduction Co., 87; value of estate at death, 87; 1956 value of his original Pittsburgh Reduction Co. stock, 87; his letter rejecting cryolite bath unavailable to Judge Taft, 100; his letter on first hearing of Bradley patent, 101-2; his profits in Pittsburgh Reduction Co. stock, 104; stories attributing to him origin of modern aluminum process, 125; evidence that he appropriated someone else's electric-furnace idea, 125; effect of aluminum monopoly on his reputation, 126. *See also* Hall process
Hall's Lockport sojourn, his difficulties with external combustion heat, 70, 73; why he did not employ electric furnace, 71; his difficulties with copper anodes, 72; he later admits failure of his process there, 72-73; why he could not use large crucibles, 73-74; facilities available to him, 74-75, 77-78; reasons for his difficulties, 75; he receives all facilities requested, 77; various witnesses testify that his experiments were unsuccessful, 78-79; why Cowles Co. was unimpressed by his record there, 79-80; text of patent covering version of process he was advocating there, 183-88
Hall's relations with Cowles brothers, his invention comes after their electric furnace, 64; his first meeting with them, 65; he tells them modern aluminum

process no good, 70; he claims that they broke agreement, 80-81; he leaves Lockport to join Pittsburgh Reduction Co., 83; he first adopts their electric-furnace idea, 83-84

Hall, Julia, testimony that Hall used cryolite bath, 77

Hall patent, its owner gains ascendancy in United States, 95

Hall process, his description of, 15-16; another description of, 17; first to produce aluminum commercially, 19; feature of modern aluminum process not covered by, 19-20; option granted to Cowles Co., 65-66; variation advocated by Hall at Lockport, 67; bath for alumina not simple cryolite, 76; conflicting testimony on ingredients of bath, 77; terms of Cowles option on, 80; *Cassier's Magazine* article describing bath mixture, 84-85; its patent claims broad enough to cover simple cryolite, 85; text of patent for, 178-83

Hammond, John Winthrop (General Electric historian), says Cowles brothers invented electric furnace, 36-37; describes Bradley's converter, 51

Hand, Judge Learned, his opinion on status of an issued patent, 57-58

Harvard College, receives Cowles silicon carbide specimen, 45-46

Haskell, George D., attempts to engage in aluminum production, 117; sues Duke estate charging breach of contract, 117

Héroult, Paul Louis Toussaint, his part in originating modern aluminum process, 15; description of his discovery, 17, 91-92; turns from aluminum to alloys, 18, 92; feature of modern aluminum process not covered by

his patent, 19-20; Cowles electric furnace antedates his invention, 64; his U.S. patent application precedes Hall's, 64; rumors of his activities stimulate Cowles brothers, 69; first adopts modern aluminum process, 86-87; early life of, 91; helped by learning about Cowles electric furnace, 93; early visit with grandfather in England, 96; helps organize United States Aluminum Metal Co., 96; employed as engineer by Southern Aluminium Co., 96, 114; his electric furnace for steel industry, 96; death of, 114; text of his most important patent, 174-78; text of his aluminum bronze patent, 188-90; text of his British patent, 190-96; mentioned, 126

Héroult process, German investors buy patent rights for, 94; its early use in Switzerland described by Albert Stetson, 95; gains ascendancy in Europe, 95

Hobbs, John, his role misunderstood by Judge Taft, 85-86

Hunt, Alfred E., provides funds to promote Hall's idea, 82

Hunt, Dr. T. Sterry, says Cowles brothers invented electric furnace, 36; describes production of aluminum by Cowles brothers, 38; attributes to Cowles brothers process for producing aluminum, 40

Hydroelectric power, introduced by Cowles brothers at Lockport, 35

Incandescent electric lighting, introduction of, 11

Industrial revolution, patent offices outgrowth of, 14

Interference between Hall and Héroult, declared by Patent Office, 68